BEVERLY SASSOON'S

BEAUTY FOR ALWAYS

BEVERLY SASSOON'S
BEAUTY FOR ALWAYS

Beverly Sassoon

with Barbara Wilkins

Illustrated by Bill Moore

AVON
PUBLISHERS OF BARD, CAMELOT, DISCUS AND FLARE BOOKS

AVON BOOKS
A division of
The Hearst Corporation
959 Eighth Avenue
New York, New York 10019

Copyright © 1982 by Beverly Sassoon
Text illustrations Copyright © 1982 by Bill Moore
Front and back cover photographs Copyright © 1982
by Harry Langdon
Design by Sheldon Winicour
Published by arrangement with the authors
Library of Congress Catalog Card Number: 82-1680
ISBN: 0-380-80572-3

Library of Congress Cataloging in Publication Data
Sassoon, Beverly.
    Beauty for always.
    Includes index.
    1. Beauty, Personal.   I. Wilkins, Barbara.
II. Title.
RA778.S258   646.7′042   82-1680
ISBN 0-380-80572-3   AACR2

First Avon Printing, September, 1982

Contents

v

BEVERLY SASSOON'S
BEAUTY FOR ALWAYS

I

The Beginnings of Beauty

1

Prologue

The winter of 1980 was not the best of times in southern California. For weeks, sheets of rain had tumbled houses off their hillside perches, splintering them into jagged piles of wood and scattered shingles. Empty cars bobbed like toys down new rivers that were usually peaceful canyons connecting Los Angeles to the vast, flat San Fernando Valley where I grew up.

The winter of 1980 was not the best of times for me, either. The fury of the endless storm seemed to reflect my own inner chaos. Several months earlier, I has asked my husband of thirteen years, Vidal Sassoon, for a divorce. Ever since, my family and my friends had been asking me if I was sure I knew what I was doing, if I was sure I was doing the right thing. I brushed off their concern. Of course I was doing the right thing, I assured them.

When I awoke alone in bed in the glorious, new home into which our family had moved only a few months before, it was still black outside. Lightning crackled through the sodden sky and thunder boomed in its wake. I was paralyzed with anxiety. Suddenly, the full impact of my decision sank in. Now I asked myself the questions my family and friends had been asking me: Was I doing the right thing? Wouldn't it be easier, better for me, for Vidal, for our four children, to stay married, to smile?

Any mother will understand what I did then. I forced myself to slip out of bed to see if my children were all right.

Catya, eleven years old, with her blue eyes and curly brown hair, slept alone for once. My Catya is the Perle Mesta of Beverly Hills. With her big heart, she is a child who wants to share herself. Usually, a gang of girl friends in their sleeping bags is bedded down in her room.

Elan, ten, was born on his father's birthday. People have said that he looks as if he is Vidal's clone. We have great expectations for Elan. He's a bright boy who is good at school; he's an athlete who is good at soccer and baseball. With his gregarious ways, he's an adaptable boy who gets along with everybody. Elan has been moved from New York to Beverly Hills, from house to house. He's adapted to the change from a mother who was always around to a mother who was at school, to a mother who was at work, to a mother who was away on business for days at a time. And now he would have to adapt to divorce.

David is eight. When we adopted our half-black child, he was two years old. His white mother had just given him away for the second time. Nobody knows who his father is. In those first days after David became a member of our family, it wasn't unusual to come home to find a fire truck or a plumber's truck in the driveway. David was bewildered and angry. He is the only one of our children who goes to a private school because he needs to have definite limits set for him—he needs to know how far he can go. His anger hasn't diminished. Aside from loving him, all I can do for David is to try my best to equip him with the tools and security he has to have to deal with the anger that so often manifests itself in socially unacceptable behavior. If nothing else, David will have the option of getting a good education, which will give him the chance to make his own choices.

What were my options? When I married Vidal, it seemed to me that there was only one happy ending, the traditional one of husband and home and children. Here I was trading that happy ending for uncharted territory, for all the unknowns I was going to have to face myself.

Eden is our baby. At seven years old, with her thick, blondish hair and her wise, brown eyes, she is the most independent and secure of all the children. It is difficult for me to get angry with her because she turns everything into a joke. I watch this little girl of mine as she deals with her world. How would the future be for Eden? What would divorce do to that wonderful sense of security?

Should I have waited until my children were grown before I asked for a divorce? When Eden turns eighteen, I'll only be forty-three. Vidal, though, will be sixty-two. It just didn't seem fair to stay in the marriage. It wasn't fair to me and it wasn't fair to Vidal. But what about the children? Wouldn't it be more responsible to give them the continuity of a two-parent home?

The rain dinned endlessly as the night turned into a sullen dawn. I crawled back into the bed my husband and I had shared so briefly. Vidal had joked with a reporter a few weeks earlier that if I had spent more time in the kitchen things would be different. When I read that interview I wondered just what those words meant. I knew it was a joke, a way to turn aside the painful question of why we had decided to divorce. But what were the implications? Would things have been different if I had spent more time in the kitchen? Would I still be the same narrow, malleable post-adolescent Vidal had married? Would I have remained the adoring, awe-struck accessory to his glittering life that I had been then? Would I just have stopped growing? Can any person really expect that of another person?

Let's say that time can be stopped, that experience can be stopped. Suppose I had stayed twenty-one years old. Would Vidal want that? Would anybody?

What Vidal said was a joke, of course, but to me that joke epitomizes the attitude many men have toward the growing number of women no longer content with traditional feminine occupations, the women who are exercising options we didn't even know we had only a few years ago. But, we're not the same people we were then.

Selflessness is no longer appropriate behavior. It is dawning on us that there is more to the life of a woman than to be somebody's wife, somebody's mother. More and more of us are finding that it feels good to be responsible for our own actions. It feels good when we test and extend ourselves and find that we can do what we set out to do. As we attempt to live the constructive lives we are beginning to believe to be our right, each of us must fall back on herself to find out just what that constructive life is. We must discover individually how to begin the odyssey to self-discovery. Society, too, is awakening to the fact that women are its vast, unused resource, a resource that must now be used to keep the wheels of the economy turning as the two-paycheck family makes the quantum jump from luxury to necessity. Society applauds us for our new efforts, but it can't help us; it offers no guidelines. We are pioneers.

Did I finally doze that troubled night? I suppose I did, because when the alarm clock buzzed that morning at 6:30, it called me to a crystal awareness of the instant. I was suddenly aware of me, of Beverly, of a separate person having a separate set of experiences at a given time. There was the beautiful room I was in, the soft pillows and the pretty, pressed sheets. When I was married I slept in old flannel nightgowns. Now that I was alone, I was wearing a black number with spaghetti straps and a bit of black lace because it made me feel good.

It comes to me that I can't turn back. When I think of the years I spent with Vidal, the years when I developed into the person I am now, it sounds ungrateful. But, as the opportunities to grow presented themselves, I took them. Because I took them, I grew. And I'm not sorry. I wouldn't turn back into the little girl I was when I met Vidal for anything. I couldn't anyway: She doesn't exist anymore. Maybe this is what so many American women are saying today. We can't stunt ourselves anymore. We can't stay where we were, no matter how much we would like to, no matter what the guilts involved, no matter how uncertain the path ahead.

As my concept of myself has changed, as the concept of the way so many women see themselves is changing, so has my concept of beauty changed. When I was growing up, you tried to be beautiful to attract and catch a man. Today, beauty and health are expressions of self-pride. In the following pages I'll try to share with you everything that I've learned, first as an amateur and then as a professional in my field of health and beauty. With this information, I think that you will be able to take stock of yourself with a critical but realistic eye and set about developing a fast, easy, fun program to help you to be the very best you can be and keep you there. You will see that I don't believe that developing such a program should be a painful process that is only fast, easy and fun once you've gotten there. I think you'll find ways to get started that will fit as easily and effortlessly into your life as they have into mine. Every woman can attain—and maintain—beauty.

I'm beginning a new stage in my life, but at this point I approach it with all I've learned from my own experiences as Vidal's wife, as a mother, as a student, as a career woman. In these pages, I'll discuss these phases of my development, too, because it seems to me they reflect the lives of many American women.

I can't go back to the carefree times of no responsibility, nor would I want to. I approach this stage in my life as a person of strength, as a person who has sifted through what I have learned, discarded what doesn't apply, and kept what does. I've maximized my potential to make the strongest possible presentation of myself. And I did it for me. What I'm saying is that I like myself, that I think I'm worth taking care of. This life of mine is the only one I'm going to have, and it's up to me to make the most of it.

❧ 2 ❧

The Fast, Easy, Fun Morning Routine That Works for Me

First as an enthusiastic amateur married to a professional in the health and beauty field and later as a professional myself, I have always been eager to experiment with new methods. I have also never lost sight of the goal of my experimentation: to attain the greatest possible benefit with the least possible effort. In other words, I want to be as healthy and beautiful as I can be, but I want to pay the lowest price to get that way.

Does that sound a little narcissistic? A bit shallow and self-absorbed? If I were a professional in any other field than health and beauty, I don't think it would. If I were an accountant, for example, obviously my goal would be to attain the greatest possible benefit for my client with the least effort. Otherwise, he would have to pay for my inefficiency because it would have taken more of my time as I muddled around. If I were a truck driver, going to San Francisco from Los Angeles via Denver wouldn't make sense. If I were a mathematician, I would be drummed out of the corps if my solutions weren't arrived at in the simplest way. In mathematics, by definition elegance *is* simplicity.

And so it should be with health and beauty. I can't figure out why taking care of yourself has to be a time-consuming ordeal. It's almost as if women feel they should be punished for being selfish enough to want to look good and to feel good. Well, I've never thought that virtue arises from masochism.

When I see joggers and runners sweating and straining for that next breath, I wonder about people who seem to get their pleasure out of pain. I know those joggers and runners would get the same results, or better, from a lovely stroll while they looked at the flowers. The only time I would consider running would be if somebody were chasing me with a dangerous weapon in hand.

What I do to stay in shape and look as good as possible must meet three criteria. I accept the fact that it is important to work up a sweat to get rid of the body's impurities, but that is just about the only hardship I do accept. Otherwise, what I do must be easy, fast and fun.

And it's not that my methods of health and beauty care are so automatic that they come as naturally as brushing my teeth. What I do find is that if I haven't exercised for a long time, I hear myself complaining about feeling exhausted. My body is out of tune, and it's letting me know it. I listen to my body. That's one of the most important things I have learned about health and beauty care.

Within a month or less of resuming my exercises I start to notice that my energy level has increased. My mind is more clear than when I don't exercise and it functions with less fuzz. These benefits are even more important to me than the obvious ones of keeping away those unwanted bumps and bulges, or keeping my muscles in tone so they won't atrophy.

Like everybody else, I am exercising to make the most out of the body I already have. But I exercise slowly at my own pace, to music. I make sure I am in front of a mirror so I can monitor the grace of my motions, the geometry of my body.

TWO-MINUTE BED STRETCH

I can't say enough in favor of stretching, and I always manage to find the few minutes a day it takes to do it. Stretching gives me the confidence that comes with the feeling of firming up. It relieves tension and it relaxes me. When I wake up in the morning, I don't believe in throwing my body into shock by jumping out of bed. Rather, I coax my body into wakefulness with an easy warm-up in bed that takes no more than two minutes.

Lying on my back, I clasp my hands behind my head and stretch my back muscles by drawing my elbows in toward each other. I hold the position for a few seconds. Then I rotate my chin forward onto my chest and hold for a few seconds.

Because I have a tendency to retain fluids, my hands feel fat in the morning. I raise my arms and work my wrists, rotating them and shaking out my fingers. I work my toes, flexing them and unflexing them. I rotate my ankles for a few seconds. I pull my right knee up and hold it in the crook of my elbow, then repeat the process with my left knee. I concentrate on my breathing. I've stretched my muscles and my frame, helped my heart and lungs. As my blood begins to circulate, I can feel my face becoming pinker and healthier looking. Most important, the whole process of bed stretching has been easy and gentle. There will be stress enough when I face the world outside.

THE THREE-MINUTE SENSUAL SHOWER

In the warm shower, I use a hard sponge, called a Loofah, on my body. The Loofah is a member of the squash family, and some people grow them in their gardens. I bought mine in a drugstore for less than a dollar. If my skin were oily, I would use a slightly abrasive soap with an oat-protein base. (To find out if a soap has an oat-protein base read the list of ingredients on the back of the package.) Because my skin tends to be a bit dry, I use a hard-milled, super-fatted coconut oil-based soap. I wet the Loofah and work the soap into it. Using a circular motion, I massage my upper and outer thighs, my buttocks and the backs of my arms to bring the blood to the surface of my body, to get my circulation going and to get rid of the dead skin. Then I wash the rest of my body, stretching to reach my feet. Again, listen to your body. If your skin is extremely sensitive, the action of a Loofah may be too abrasive.

THE APRÈS SENSUAL SHOWER BONUS STRETCH

As I step from the shower, my skin is smooth and my circulation is good. Hot water would have opened my pores, allowing moisture to escape. Instead, I showered in warm water, which has left my skin looking plump and rosy. I dry my body only slightly before I moisturize. My object is to seal the moisture into my pores by applying to it the protective coat we know as moisturizer.

Drying and moisturizing take a couple of minutes. The stretches I do while I moisturize are bonus stretches because they are done at the same time. Facing the mirror, with feet apart and toes pointed forward, I alternate rubbing moisturizer down each side of my body, working my waist and legs, while keeping knees straight.

To moisturize my feet, calves, thighs and hips, I put one leg on the bathroom sink. (If you don't feel quite this agile, use the toilet seat.) With my leg on the counter, and my toes pointed, I start to moisturize. I bend forward, exhaling, from the waist as I try to reach my toes. I stretch as I apply the moisturizer, loosening the ankle area, the calves, loosening the spine, expanding and contracting the vertebrae. I inhale as I straighten up.

THE CLEAN TEETH BONUS STRETCH

The stretch you do while you're cleaning your teeth is a bonus because it costs you nothing in terms of time. You're cleaning your teeth anyway. I lean over and make my back level like a table, pushing my buttocks out. This stretches the hamstring muscles in the thighs, calves and ankles. I contract my stomach muscles, push them out, and contract them again.

THE TWO-MINUTE GLOWING FACE

The one element of health and beauty care that can't be put off until tomorrow is to wash, tone and moisturize my face, both morning and evening. Thanks to the fact that the cosmetics industry spends millions of dollars in research each year, we now have the chance to use quality products to take care of our skin. The old wives' tale that soap should not be used on the skin is no longer true, and we now have the option to use soap, or a quality cleansing cream, or both.

Cleansing the Skin

Because my skin is on the dry side, I use a soap with super-fatted coconut oil. If your skin is oily, use a more abrasive soap, possibly one with an oat-protein base for a deeper cleansing action. Combination skin should be washed with a mild castile soap. In all cases, soap should be washed off the face with tepid, running water. Hot water opens the pores and lets the moisture escape. The face should be patted dry very gently.

Bonus Chin Exercises

When I wash my face, I tuck my lower lip over my bottom teeth, which tightens my neck. It is the only facial exercise I do. After all, we pull and push and tug at our faces all day long when we smile, or grimace, or change expression. It is because of all this use that the face naturally gets that I also suggest patting the face dry very gently.

Toning

The oil-producing sebaceous glands are around the nose, mouth, chin and forehead. Cosmetics companies put out toners, astringents and clarifying lotions for dry, oily and normal skin. Again, just read the list of ingredients on the package, and you will find the product that is right for your skin. All of these products have an alcohol content, but I try to stay away from those with high alcohol contents as alcohol dries the skin. I saturate a cotton ball with toner, dilute it with a few drops of tepid water from the tap, and apply it only to my forehead, nose, around my mouth and chin. then I splash it off with tepid water and gently pat my skin dry.

Moisturizing

A question I am always asked at my lectures on the fast, easy, fun way to health and beauty is whether the skin should be moisturized as part of a skin care program. Because we begin to lose the natural elasticity of the skin at about the age of seventeen or eighteen, my feeling is that moisturizer is vital for all skins, male as well as female. Moisturizer is not, of course, absorbed into the skin, and its use is only a temporary solution to dryness. What it does do is seal in the skin's natural moisture. Moisturizing both morning and evening helps to normalize the skin and bring it into proper balance.

I stay away from any moisturizer that contains paraffin, beeswax, or petroleum jelly. I've just cleaned my face and I'm not about to clog up my pores with any solid. The moisturizers I use have a rice oil base, something light that permits the natural exchange of oxygen and carbon dioxide. I start to moisturize at the top of my bosom, work upward over my chest and neck, and moisturize my face to my hairline. My goal is a clean, clear, healthy complexion. Only at that point do I feel I have the option of applying products such as foundations and blushers, eye makeup and lipstick. A clean face is a necessity; makeup is a luxury.

In the evening, I repeat this simple cleansing process with a couple of variations. I do use a cleansing cream to take off my makeup. When I was a teen-ager, I found that baby oil worked well to take off my eye makeup. I've never found a product that does it better. Then it's soap, toner, and moisturizer again. Because there are no oil glands around the eyes, I also use an eye cream at night to ward off the tiny wrinkles that inevitably appear in an area with no oil to feed it. Eye cream is designed to be used around the eyes. Other products aren't. It must be emphasized that almost all of these products, including moisturizer, should be kept away from the eyes. When I speak to women's groups, it always surprises me how few women know that.

Because there is so much to do in the morning to meet the 7:30 out-the-front-door deadline the children and I share, it has been a habit with me to lay out the clothes I am going to wear the night before. Even on languid mornings, there is no way pulling on my jeans and a sweater can take more than thirty seconds. I pull a comb through my short, well-cut, wash-and-wear hair, spend five minutes at my "no makeup" makeup, and then I'm ready to go downstairs to join the kids in the kitchen for breakfast.

It's a madhouse as they wolf down their bacon and eggs, squabbling and giggling. I brew my cup of tea, my first vice of the day. As I want to stress, nobody is perfect; I'm certainly not. I'm a woman with a busy life and many demands on my time. I don't see how I could ever be perfect. All I can do is the best I can. While I'm standing at the stove dipping my teabag into a cup of hot water, I stretch. I place my hand on the counter, tucking in my pelvis. The teabag gets dipped as I rise up on my toes and return, rise up on my toes and return. I know that everybody should have some kind of breakfast, but sometimes I do, and sometimes I don't.

If, like me, you find it hard to face scrambled eggs, toast and the other things that constitute a "real breakfast," there is an easy solution to the problem—a Vitality Drink that will give you long-lasting energy throughout the day with a minimum of fuss.

This high-protein drink provides just what you need to start the day properly:

Vitality Drink

1 tablespoon powdered
    protein from a health
    food store or
    drugstore
1$^1/_2$ teaspoons granular
    lecithin (from a health
    food store or
    drugstore

1 small banana (or a peach or
    berries in season
1 raw egg
1 cup low-fat or
    nonfat milk

Toss everything into the container of a blender and process for thirty seconds.

Have a slice of whole wheat toast with this drink and you have the perfect high protein, high energy food to start the day.

After I finish my breakfast, I glance at my watch and see that it's almost 7:30. I hurry the kids along, then get into my car and tell myself that I've done the very best with what I have—and it's been fast, easy and fun.

3

Beverly Adams of Burbank

My father, Wayne Adams, a tall, dark, shy man, is a seventh generation American of Irish descent who was born in Illinois. He was
a baseball player, a pitcher for the St. Louis Cardinals when the
Second World War started. He joined the United States Air Force
and found himself stationed in Edmonton, Alberta, Canada, where
he met my mother, Tillie Halwa. Her parents had emigrated to
Canada from Poland and she was a first generation Canadian. I
was born there, after the Second World War was over. My parents
were delighted, but pictures show a baby who was anything but
promising. With my pointed head and big ears I think I was the
kind of baby who evoked remarks like, ''Well, there *is* a baby.''

After my father was discharged from the Air Force, our little
family moved to South Bend, Indiana. A baseball player's working
life is a short one, and he had to find something to do for a living.
He moved from job to job trying to find his niche.

During the war, women en masse moved into the jobs vacated
by the men who had gone off to fight. As soon as the war was
over, they rushed back to their homes to play out the traditional
roles of wife and mother. My mother was a woman of her time.
The only time I remember being left with a baby-sitter was when
she went to the hospital to have a miscarriage.

I wasn't a very healthy child. I spent so much time in bed with

17

childhood illnesses that I thought that was what all children did. I became very good at entertaining myself, playing alone for hours, carrying on conversations among my paper dolls.

I had walked at nine months and by the time I entered kindergarten at a nearby Catholic school, I could also read. When I was in the first grade, I came down with rheumatic fever and it was back to bed. I missed nearly a year of school and my mother's concern for me increased.

Because I was always ill, I was considered a weakling.

My father had been working at the Studebaker Corporation but things weren't going well for him. My parents decided to move back to Canada, partly, I suspect, because my mother missed her family. Our stay in Canada was brief. My parents had forgotten how cold it was there, and we were soon on our way again. We eventually ended up in southern California where my parents rented a little one-bedroom apartment in Burbank.

After the grim, gray streets of South Bend and the icy temperatures of Canada, Burbank was like a paradise to me. There was sun nearly every day, and I was charmed by the towering palm trees. I could pick oranges from the trees that grew in abundance in the neighbors' gardens. Everything was clean and new, and filled with promise.

My father found a job as a hydraulic lab technician for Sterer Engineering, which makes valves for airplanes. Every morning he would go off to work dressed all in white. He still works there, and my parents still live in the same little house we moved into that year.

I was eight years old, a chubby, short, little girl covered with freckles. There was nothing special about me at all. Like all children, I wanted to belong. I joined the Girl Scouts, and when we were settled, I began to make friends. Because I wasn't attractive, I didn't think I was entitled to like boys. It was no wonder I was a chunky child. At home, my mother prepared the same meat and potatoes she had cooked in colder climates. When I went out, it was a big treat to have a hamburger, French fries and a chocolate malt.

Still, I loved the movies and I was madly in love with Elvis Presley and Troy Donahue. I couldn't wait to get home from school each afternoon to watch Walt Disney's *Mickey Mouse Club*. I felt there was something glamorous about the fact that Walt Disney Productions was also in Burbank.

None of us ever looked at a magazine, and we had no idea of

fashion, but my girl friends and I played at being teen-agers. Oh, how we wanted to grow up! We experimented with scarfs on our heads and with lipstick. We pretended we were driving our own convertibles as we scooted around the streets of Burbank on our bicycles.

My life was as placid as the streets of Burbank. I was a good student, though, and I had a retentive mind. My vision of what my future would be was expanding. I couldn't decide whether to be a doctor or to be president of the United States. I had the feeling that whatever I did would have impact and some kind of meaning.

In the larger environment of junior high school, there were social groups that hadn't existed in the simpler, smaller grammar school. There were the popular kids, the brains, the so-so kids and the wimps. I never felt I belonged with any of them. I floated from group to group, and settled, finally, on student affairs. I was on the Student Council and I was designated an Outstanding Citizen of Jordan Junior High. I was elected Student Body President in the first semester of the ninth grade, and I didn't see anything odd about the fact that I was the first girl to be elected to that post. I was reelected Student Body President the next semester. And the braces I had worn for two years were removed. I now had nice, straight teeth and a pretty smile. Having my braces removed was a rite of passage into the world of teen-age dating.

When I was a teen-ager, my mother used to make me go to "recreation dances" that were held for all the kids. I hated to go and I suffered agonies of shyness and fear. Like many things, it was all right once I got there.

My girl friends and I had started experimenting with lipsticks when we were ten. Once I was in my junior year of high school, I added eye makeup to my repertoire. I had Cleopatra eyes. I was destroying my hair with back combing. I would sleep with toilet paper wrapped around it. I wasn't concerned about my weight. I took my body for granted. It was even a kick to go up a size. It meant that I was growing up, becoming an adult. The only thing that stayed the same was my AA bra size.

At fourteen, a boy asked me out. With another couple, we went to Disneyland. By the time I was a sixteen-year-old cheerleader in the eleventh grade, my girl friends and I were hanging out at a teen-age disco. I was always the one who could get the car from my parents, and even though I had to come home at eleven o'clock, I felt very grown up. My life could have been right out of a beach party movie.

I had also revised my career goals—downward. I had given up the notion of becoming either a doctor or the president of the United States. I decided instead that I might become a dental hygienist. That seemed to be a goal I could achieve, and it was also a socially acceptable profession for a girl.

When my girl friends and I weren't at Bob's Big Boy, wolfing down hamburgers and malts and flirting with the boys in the next car, we would go to the Pickwick Recreation Center. One of the attractions at Pickwick was an ice skating rink, and I yearned to learn how to ice skate. My parents couldn't really afford the ice skating lessons I wanted to take, but I found out that if I got a job in the sports shop selling bathing suits, ice skating costumes and ice skates, I could get lessons free. One of the highlights of my life at that time was an ice skating exhibition. I was one of the human barrels the man giving the exhibit jumped over.

A teen-age dance party on one of the local television stations originated from Pickwick. People from the show would come into the shop to borrow clothes for the fashion segment. They needed somebody to model the clothes and I was asked if I wanted to do it. Of course I did. I was delighted, and my mother was ecstatic. I was also beginning to enter beauty contests—and win them. I was Miss Pacific Ocean Park, an amusement park at Santa Monica beach. I was Miss Queen of Speed, which, in those days, had to do with drag racing. I was Miss San Fernando Valley.

Obviously, I was beginning to realize that I was no longer the plain, chunky, freckled little girl I had been. People began to tell me how pretty I was. At that stage of my life, I was very much impressed with the way people reacted to me. I wanted the admiration of my peers. I wanted my parents to approve of me, and I wanted to be admired by their friends. I think it was the admiration that made me enter the beauty contests. When I was a beauty contestant, people looked at me as if I were a cow, but I thought that if I got that little banner it meant that I was beautiful, that I had a nice figure, a nice smile. In those simpler days, that was the level of approval that girls were conditioned to want.

I was asked to model at industrial shows where you stand around next to a bathtub and smile. I also did an RC Cola commercial with Art Linkletter. I was the All-American Girl with my hair in a flip, my pixie band, and my bottle of RC Cola.

At the studio, while I was filming the commercial, Ozzie Nelson, who was on the very popular *Ozzie and Harriet* show, saw me. He asked me to read for him, and I got a part. That year, I rode on the Helms Bakery float in the Rose Parade. I was freezing and I had cramps in my face from smiling. I smiled and smiled as I wondered why I was doing such things to myself. Why was I going through the anxiety and the discomfort? I guess there must have been an ego thing I didn't realize I had.

Meanwhile, I was working and making money. I bought myself a white Chevrolet Impala with a red interior, and it was all very glamorous and exciting. But, the girls I thought were my friends began to pull away from me. And, at first, the boys I dated enjoyed the fact that I was on television and entering beauty contests and winning them. Later, they seemed to find it threatening.

After I graduated from high school, my agent, Dale Garrick, took me to New York to make the rounds of the agencies there. We stayed with his mother in Brooklyn. Every day, I would go into Manhattan and pound the pavement, dropping off my composite at the advertising agencies. I didn't get any jobs from the trip, but I did meet a lot of people.

That fall, I enrolled in Valley State College to become a dental hygienist. I was working and making money, but not on a regular basis, so it was important to have a way to make a living. College wasn't what I thought it would be. I had visions of student parties and sitting under a big tree, studying with my friends. Instead, there were tales of student riots drifting down from Berkeley.

I was also being offered small jobs, and I had the feeling that if I didn't take them, they might not be there when I was ready for them. And I was having fun. The world I was living in on a part-time basis was glamorous. I was getting my ego stroked, and my social horizons were expanding. After a few weeks at Valley State, I dropped out. College wasn't going to go away. I would get back to it at another time. I didn't realize how long it would be.

In the beginning, I had felt terribly nervous about meeting people I had only heard about, but that anxiety vanished quickly. I was much more interested in who they were as people than I was in what my reactions were. I stopped thinking about myself and I started to think about them. I was starting to learn the game.

I went to casting calls where I would be one of thirty girls being considered for a part. I also had, say, a couple of lines on the *Joey Bishop Show*, or I would turn up as a nurse on *Dr. Kildare*. I did more little parts on television. I also got a couple of bits in movies at Paramount, including *Roustabout* and *Girl Happy*, which both starred Elvis Presley. I was still living at home. I hadn't yet turned eighteen, but I was feeling pretty sophisticated.

One day, when I went out to the parking lot at Paramount, I found my car wouldn't start. What seemed to be a mile-long limou-

sine pulled up alongside me and the window went down. It was
Elvis Presley who offered to give me a lift home. I called home and
told my mother very casually that I was having car problems, but
that somebody was giving me a lift home. She asked who was
bringing me home and I told her it was Elvis Presley. Then I realized that when I got home everybody in Burbank would be lurking
behind the bushes to get a look at him.

"Please, Mother," I said. "Don't say anything to anybody."

"Of course, I won't," she said indignantly.

On the way to my house, Elvis asked me if I was free for dinner that night. I was floored: I couldn't imagine anybody driving
back to Burbank twice on one day. When we got to my house, it
was just as I had expected. There were the neighbors, all in curlers,
peering out from behind every bush.

Elvis didn't come to pick me up for dinner that night, but his
car did. I was driven to his house in Beverly Hills where we were
going to eat. He never went out. There were people everywhere.
Somebody was playing a guitar, somebody else was singing. There
were people standing around talking at the bar or watching football
on television. Telephones were ringing. There were girls standing
around outside the house, hoping to be invited in.

Elvis was a perfect gentleman. It was, "Yes, ma'am," and
"No, sir." When he was with me, he gave me all of his attention.
In the months we were dating, I never saw him take so much as
one drink.

At that stage, I was still consciously trying to keep my perspec-
tive of my new career. I knew my looks could get me through the
door, but after that it was up to me. I made it my business to know
what was happening behind the camera and not just in front of it.
After a screen test, I was offered a contract with Columbia. The
$250 a week I was to receive at the beginning lowered my income,
but it was a chance for me to learn and expand.

My first starring part was in *Winter A Go Go.* Then I did the
first of the Matt Helm films, *The Silencers,* with Dean Martin. I
played Lovey Kravezit, Matt Helm's secretary. In one scene, Dean
Martin was on a big, round bed at one end of a room. The bed
would tilt him into a bathtub as big as a small swimming pool
where I would be waiting. There wasn't much to my wardrobe.
Pasties were glued on me, and I wore a little G-string bottom. I was
shy and embarrassed in front of the hundreds of people who were
always standing around on the set. I got to the point where I would
walk directly into the tank wearing a bathrobe. Dean and I spent
five days in that bathtub.

When the film was finished, the studio sent me out to promote it, along with a public relations woman to look after me. Glamorous it wasn't. It was getting up at four in the morning to do the early television shows. It would be, ''Well, here's a starlet,'' which I hated. Press conferences for the movie would be held at hotel swimming pools which for the occasion would be filled with bubble bath. I would come out in my little costume with a towel and walk into the water.

I was making tentative moves toward being on my own, but I just wasn't ready. I would rent an apartment and move out, and then I would turn around and move right back in with my family. I also felt I should be making more progress in my career. I knew I wanted to get away from the cute, stupid, little girl roles. I didn't really mind that I was playing some yo-yo in the Mickey Rooney film, *How to Stuff a Wild Bikini,* but I wanted to play well-defined characters. I wanted to be Audrey Hepburn. She was sophisticated, but she wasn't tough. Women liked her as well as men. I wanted to have those qualities, too.

It was 1965, and the student riots and the antiwar demonstrations that were commonplace might as well have been happening on the moon. I was living at home, so I had lots of money to buy clothes. I was always out with somebody. There were Ferraris, Jaguars and an occasional limousine in front of my house. The neighbors got a big kick out of it.

I had toured parts of America to promote films, but when I was asked to go to Rio de Janiero for a film festival, I was thrilled. Some of the people on the trip were Jan Murray, Troy Donahue, Yvette Mimieux and Rita Thiel, who was to be my roommate. We were barely in the door to drop off our luggage before we were out the door to see Rio. Two or three film crews were shooting in the city, the festivities connected with the film festival were underway and here we were, with a strange new city to explore. The clubs stayed open until six in the morning, and we were always walking out of a club into broad daylight.

I was scheduled to be in Rio de Janiero for two weeks. Instead I was offered a role in one of the movies being filmed there, and I stayed for two months. No sooner was I back in Burbank then the studio sent me off again to a film festival in Argentina. My casual attitude to my health caught up with me when I got home again. I came down with mononucleosis. It was all I could do to walk from my bed to the bathroom and it was six months before I was able to start my next film.

I had been threatening to move out again. At the doctor's office one day, I met Elaine Gaskell, the registered nurse who worked in the office. She mentioned that her roommate was leaving. With Elaine and another nurse, I moved into a two-bedroom, two-bathroom apartment a few blocks east of the studio in Hollywood. With three girls in one apartment, the phone was usually ringing off the hook. We didn't see too much of each other, but when we were all home, we lived on raw carrots, cold hot dogs and tea.

When my birthday came around that year, the studio told me I was being sent to London to co-star in a film called *Torture Garden*, with Jack Palance, Burgess Meredith and Peter Cushing. I was to leave for England the day after my twenty-first birthday.

· 4 ·

Thoughts About Adolescence

When I was a teen-ager, I went to Bob's Big Boy to eat hamburgers, French fries and chocolate malts. I attacked my hair until it towered three feet above my head. I covered my face with panstick so that it looked as if I were wearing a mask, and administered the coup de grace with enough eyeliner and false eyelashes and mascara to make me look not only like a road company Cleopatra, but hard, and years older than my age. Like most adolescents, I burned off a lot of energy with dancing, ice skating and a lot of random motion.

From the point of view of health and beauty, adolescence is the best of times and the worst of times. The best of it is a firm young body, supple skin that has not yet begun to lose its elasticity, the natural energy and endurance of youth. Best of all, adolescence is the time to begin a health and beauty care program that will become, as time goes on, as much a habit as brushing your teeth and washing your face. It can be the worst of times, too, if you are plagued with some of the common problems of adolescence, such as acne, blemishes and dandruff.

NUTRITION

Proper nutrition includes a balanced intake of carbohydrates, fats, protein, vitamins, minerals and water. All of them are available in lean meats, fish, vegetables, fruit and dairy products. The most important concept to remember is balance. Not only is proper nutrition essential to the health of the body, but also to the health of the hair and skin.

Nobody expects a teen-ager to stay strictly away from hamburgers, jelly doughnuts, soft drinks and cream-filled cupcakes. I know I didn't. But you have to keep in mind that junk food is exactly what it is called. It does nothing for you. Try to keep junk food to a minimum, and compensate with lean meats, fish, vegetables, fruit and dairy products when you can. Remember to drink lots of water. You might want to head for the drinking fountain after each class break.

If you are the mother of a teen-ager, you can do your part by keeping the kitchen stocked with apples, oranges, raisins, nuts and other foods high in necessary nutrients. If your teen-ager can't reach for a cupcake, he'll take what's there, even if it is good for him.

BODY SHAPE

When I was an adolescent, nobody thought about developing a focused program of exercise that would keep us as firm and supple and high in energy as we could be. It was, instead, catch as catch can. We participated in those activities we liked at the time without a thought of whether they would be transferable to more sedentary times at a desk in college or in an office. I couldn't be more pleased when I see teen-agers walking briskly, playing racquet ball, or on their way to the tennis courts. Adolescence is the time to experiment, to develop an individual exercise program.

SKIN

Cleanliness is essential for controlling skin problems, such as acne and other skin blemishes. In my morning routine, I detail the proper procedure for cleaning, toning and moisturizing the face to keep it in peak condition. Read the section on proper care for either dry skin (p. 152) or oily skin (p. 152) and make a religion of following the appropriate regimen. Blackheads, which are plugs of hardened oil, can be controlled with proper skin care.

At one time it was thought that an improper diet caused acne. In fact, oily foods and junk foods do tend to aggravate acne, but here again cleanliness is the best way to control it. If your acne is severe enough to send you to the dermatologist, he will probably prescribe a daily tetracycline tablet, or some other mild antibiotic, to help to control it.

HAIR

This is the time to develop a program of washing and conditioning your hair, detailed in the general section on hair (p. 135), which will help it to look its very best.

Dandruff, another problem that plagues the teen-ager, can be controlled with one of the shampoos on the market that has been developed to control it. Again, the hair must be kept scrupulously clean. Double your efforts. If necessary, your hair can be washed daily.

I am happy to see the last of the fashion of a few years ago when all young girls wore their hair parted in the middle and as long as it could grow. This style, or nonstyle, did look good on some girls, but certainly not on everybody. Your hair should flatter your face. Consult a stylist whose work you admire and find out what suits you best.

Get rid of those stray hairs in your eyebrows by anesthetizing them with ice, and then tweezing them away, using an upward motion that follows the way they grow. If your eyebrows are bushy and grow too close together over your nose, read the section on unwanted hair (p. 145). You may decide that electrolysis, expensive but worth it, will give you the pretty brows that will enhance your face.

TEETH

Study the section on taking care of your teeth (p. 173) and start to follow each step of the program at once. Not only will you always have a pretty smile if you do, but you are at an age where you can protect yourself from future tooth loss by preventing the gum disease that causes it.

HANDS AND FEET

Giving yourself a weekly manicure and pedicure will keep your hands and feet in top condition. Details of a proper manicure and pedicure are outlined in the general section on the care of your hands and feet (p. 175). I think young girls look better and more natural if they stick to a nail polish color that is pale. Long purple or red nails should be left to the vamps in old movies on TV. Be sure to check your manicure each morning. Chipped polish looks sloppy and unattractive.

MAKEUP

The point of makeup at any age is to enhance your looks. When you are a teen-ager, makeup should enhance your naturally fresh, crisp, young look. I don't like to see foundation on a young girl. It gives a hard look. Powder should be used minimally.

I do like to see rosy cheeks. A little blusher only accentuates the fresh, young face. Lip gloss is your ally, because it moisturizes your lips and it makes them soft. I think young girls can very successfully use eyeshadow in gentle shades like taupe, lavender or light brown. Use a soft, smudge pencil as eyeliner to make your lashes look thicker and brown/black mascara no matter what your hair color for a sparkling, wide-awake look.

POSTURE

I feel a twinge of pity when I see young girls hunching over to hide their developing breasts. Bad posture gives anybody a cowed look, as if she is trying to shrink away from notice. The way you stand says a lot about the way you feel about yourself. If you try to keep your shoulders back, your chin up, and your stomach tucked in, you will be saying that you like yourself.

Even though my own children are not yet teen-agers, I often hear myself telling them what I have outlined here. I know that if they develop a proper health and beauty program at this early age, they will reap the benefits forever. The health and beauty program will have become a habit, so natural it won't take a thought to maintain. The health and beauty program you develop as an adolescent can be that way for you, too. This is the time to lay down all the foundations for a lifetime of beauty.

5

Mrs. Vidal Sassoon of London

As insular as my world as a starlet was in 1966, even I was aware of the vigor and excitement erupting in London. It was in the midst of a revolution of the working class, of Kings Road and Teddy Boys, Mods and Rockers, of the Beatles and ''I Wanna Hold Your Hand,'' of Mary Quant and Twiggy. And Vidal Sassoon.

I had seen Vidal only once, and that was on the Johnny Carson show. I was lying on the floor in the living room at my parents' house and Vidal came out wearing a silk jacket with polka dots. Then Peggy Moffatt, the famous model, came out onto the stage with the five-point, geometric haircut Vidal had given her. I thought, ''What a freak show.''

The studio had booked me into a hotel in Kensington. I would be picked up in a studio car at six in the morning for the long ride out into the country where we were shooting. I worked all day on a dark sound stage, and it was dark when I got back to the hotel. On the weekends, I spent hours at the British Museum or the Tate Gallery. I watched the changing of the guard at Buckingham Palace, visited Westminster Abbey and Westminster Cathedral. I was invited to a couple of dinner parties. Still, I was very lonely and homesick.

I was asked by the studio to do a publicity piece with the

theme, "Beverly Adams Goes Mod." In the times I had been out, I had seen that there was a difference between the way the English girls were dressed and the way I was dressed. They were all in mini-skirts, low heels, stockings made of fishnet and little sparkles, while I had my beehive hairdo, my sheath dresses and my high, high heels. A troup of people arrived to make me over. There was a stocking person, a makeup person, a shoe person and a hair person.

The hairdresser was from Vidal's salon on Bond Street. When he opened the wig box, I was horrified to see the same five-point wig I had seen on Peggy Moffatt. When the makeover was complete, I felt ridiculous and uncomfortable. Suddenly, I had all these legs, and my head felt funny without all the height I was used to carrying around.

Still, I was intrigued. When the hairdresser asked me to come to the salon one day so that he could do my hair, I decided to do it. I arrived at the Vidal Sassoon salon in my black knit dress, which fell to midcalf, and my black, high-heeled shoes with the pointy toes.

Walking through that door was like walking into a different time zone. The salon was all brown and chrome and mirrors. Rock music was blaring over the sound system, and people were dancing around. Everybody was working and bouncing and moving. Women reclined on chaises under the dryers. Somebody handed me a smock; somebody washed my hair. I had never seen anything like it. The energy level in that place was positively explosive. It was impossible not to be swept away, to be carried away by the excitement.

At some point, a man came up to me to say that Mr. Sassoon would like to take a look at my hair when I was through. I didn't know, then, that this was one of Vidal's standard lines. I was taken up four flights of stairs to his office. By the time I got to the top, I was huffing and puffing and at a total disadvantage. Vidal came out of his office and looked at my hair. He was very attractive and very soft-spoken. He seemed very young and the energy I felt from him was enormous. He asked me to turn around and he looked at the back of my hair. Of course, my hair looked exactly the same as it had when I had walked through the door of the salon. We were still shooting the film and I couldn't change it.

When Vidal asked me if I was having a good time in London, I said that I wasn't. Then he asked if he could take me to dinner a couple of nights later. When I got to the studio on Monday morning, I told the director I finally had a date. He was appalled when I told him who it was. Vidal had a reputation as a playboy and the implication was that a little girl from Burbank couldn't handle a worldly man like Vidal. Of course, that made it even more intriguing.

After he picked me up, we went first to have a drink with his friend, Sammy Davis, Jr., and then onto dinner at a gambling club above Cadogan House. There were lots and lots of bodies, and all that young, exciting, explosive English energy generated a mood of its own. I was awed and intrigued with this gentle person who seemed such an unlikely focal point for the mini-revolution that was going on.

Vidal had been born into a poor family in the East End of London. When his father died, his mother couldn't afford to support him and his brother. They spent several years in an orphanage. When she remarried, she was able to have her children with her again. All children of the working class leave school when they are fourteen to become apprentices in some field or other. In Vidal's case, he became a shampoo boy in a beauty salon and, as he told me that night, the women who came in to have their hair done looked better than when they left with it all ratted and backcombed.

Even as a teen-ager, Vidal was political. When the war in Palestine broke out in 1947, he joined the Israeli army. He loved the energy and vigor of the new country, and would have stayed there forever. But, when his stepfather had a mild heart attack, Vidal had to return to England to help take care of his family. The only thing he knew how to do was to be a hairdresser, and he went back to it. Because of his working class accent, he couldn't get a job in a good salon. He went to school to learn how to speak properly. All the time he had his own vision of how people should look, a vision of healthy, beautiful people with clean, shiny hair. By the time I met him, Vidal was in full swing.

When the evening was over, he took me back to the hotel, making a date to go to the theater a couple of nights later. I rushed to get home from the studio. By now, all those insecurities were coming out. All of a sudden, here was a man who knew more about how I should look than I did. My skirt length was all wrong. My makeup was all wrong. I must have combed my hair a dozen times. I was really uncomfortable. I shouldn't have been: Vidal never got there. Around ten that night, I got a call from somebody who said he was a friend of Vidal's. He told me Vidal was in the hospital. My Irish-Polish temper flared. "If he isn't in the hospital, he's going to be," I said, furious, as I hung up.

The friend called me back to protest that it was all true. Vidal was in the London Clinic. He had collapsed at a meeting with an attack of appendicitis, and he had just been operated on. I was very skeptical. I sent him a telegram that said, "Aren't you going a bit out of your way to break a date?" I didn't sign it. If he really was there, I knew he would know who sent it.

He called the next day. He really was there. I went zipping over to visit him. Vidal was so healthy that he looked terrific even though he had just had an operation. When he left the hospital the next day, he went to stay with his parents so they could take care of him. He called me to ask me to come to tea.

Vidal was wearing a pair of jeans and a big sweater. I sat there nervously drinking my tea, eating cookies and chatting with his parents. Vidal said he was planning to go home in a couple of days. When he did, he phoned to ask me to come over for dinner.

He lived in the remodeled servant's quarters of an old Victorian house on Curzon Street with an elevator that looked like an old iron cage. Vidal served a marvelous, elegant dinner with candlelight and wine. A couple of nights later, he was feeling well enough to go out. I began to see that no matter where we went, everybody knew him. It was *his* town and that was very exciting for me.

The film was about to end. The studio decided to send me on a ten-day promotion tour of the continent, including Paris, Frankfurt, Dusseldorf, Copenhagen and Brussels, to promote the Dean Martin films, which were just opening in Europe. As I got ready to leave for Paris, my hotel room was filled with dozens of roses. Vidal was saying "Au revoir."

He was very much on my mind as I checked into the Georges V in Paris, even though I looked upon our time together as merely a pleasant interlude. After all, he lived in England and I lived in America. Six thousand miles and two different cultures is a great gap to close.

* * *

Vidal called me in every city on the tour. While I was in Brussels, he called to ask me when I was coming back to London. Christmas was coming, and I knew I should go home. Instead, I went back to London. Vidal met me at the airport and I found that I was very, very happy to see him. He suggested that I stay in London for a little bit longer than I had planned, and that we go to a health farm together for a few days before Christmas. A health farm, I had never heard of such a thing.

Because we wanted to be together, I moved in with Vidal that night. His apartment was so small that it seemed as if there were suitcases all over the place. A couple of days later, we took off to the health farm in a burgundy Mini Minor. Grayshott Hall in Surrey was immense. It was a huge country estate with acres and acres of lawn and a mansion that accommodated between fifty and sixty people. The guests were mostly British. The young were there to lose weight, and the older people were there for a cleansing.

It was nice and warm inside Grayshott Hall, and all the people wore either little white coats or pajamas. My room was at one end of the building, and Vidal's room was at the other end. Before I knew it, I was one of those people in pajamas and a robe drinking hot water and lemon juice. I've never in my life heard so much conversation about food. Everybody was fasting, and all they talked about was the food in this London restaurant or in that Paris restaurant. It was obsessive. It was also the first time I was aware that there were people in the world who were committed to a positive attitude about taking care of themselves.

Our schedule was grueling. We would sit in hot tubs with our feet in cold tubs. Then we would sit in cold tubs with our feet in hot tubs. While we were in the shower, attendants would give us salt rubs. On the first day, we were given only hot water and lemon juice. On the second and third days we were given yogurt and grapes. At the end of the third day, we were permitted in the dining room where there were mounds and mounds of fresh-cut vegetables and all sorts of salads. By that time my stomach had gotten smaller, and it was difficult to even eat fresh vegetables and salad.

On our first day at Grayshott Hall, Vidal and I sat in his room watching a documentary about China on television. I was wearing a pink robe and a pair of his socks. He asked me to marry him, and I said, ''I thought you would never ask.''

I had never thought consciously about marrying Vidal. I don't know how it came about. He started to list all the negative things. He was Jewish and I had been raised Catholic . . . there was the age difference . . . I would have to move to England . . . I might not be able to continue my career. From the way he was talking, I decided he didn't want to marry me at all. I left the room in tears. When I got to my room, he was on the phone apologizing. I went to sleep thinking about all the things I was going to give up. My family. My career. Even my country.

I was quite willing to do it.

When I called my parents from London to say I wasn't going to be home for Christmas, there was dead silence. I had written to them about Vidal, so they knew all about him. When I told them we were planning to be married, there was another silence, and then my mother said, "Why don't you come home, dear, and we'll talk about it."

Despite what I knew lay ahead, I decided I was going to carry on and have a nice Christmas and New Year's celebration. I liked the life I had lived so far. Now I was going to marry the man I loved and live the life of a woman of the world. Nothing could make me happier than that.

Vidal changed the way I looked. My hair was short, curly and permed. My makeup had changed. Vidal had told me not to use panstick, which made my face look like a mask, and he suggested I get rid of the eyeliner. The shadow and shading I was using on my cheeks was less definite. My dresses were shorter. There were photographers taking pictures of us in front of the theater. One of the pictures was on the front page of the paper the next day. A war was going on in Vietnam and what they ran on the front page was a picture of us. I shook my head.

On Christmas Eve, we had a very French, very late dinner with friends of Vidal's, and then we all went on to midnight Mass. On New Year's Eve, we went to a party given by David Bailey, the photographer. Jean Shrimpton was there, and Roman Polanski and Sharon Tate. I knew when I got on the plane to go home to Los Angeles that there were storm clouds gathering, but all I could think about was Vidal.

Though soft and gentle, he had tremendous charisma. He was self-taught, but knew a great deal about what was going on in the world, and he hated any hint of unfairness or injustice. He was warm and very affectionate. He was making a contribution to what was going on. There were the little things, such as the way he treated people and the way he was accepted wherever we went. He was all the things I wanted in a man to whom I was attracted. Not that all the marvelous things he was did much for my own sense of security. I didn't belong, but I knew I could. He gave me confidence. He was generous and willing to share. He made me feel special and valuable, as if I were an asset to him and not just a spare part. It was as if together we completed a picture. We did have our differences in age, in religion, in our nationalities. None of it mattered, but I was concerned with how I was going to deal with my parents and the film I was scheduled to start for AIP with John Cassavetes.

I met John just about the time I got my contract with Columbia, and I wasn't looking forward to seeing him again. He did that, "Do ya' want to be in pictures, baby," routine with me, and it had been awkward and embarrassing. I left his office in tears. Now we were to co-star in a motorcycle movie called *Devil's Angels.*

My roommates couldn't believe the way I looked when I got off the plane. With my short, permed hair, I wore an orange suit with a mini-skirt and beige boots. They looked at me as if I had come from another planet, and my parents almost died when they saw me.

My roommates understood when I told them that I was going to move back home with my parents. I thought I should spend the time I had left in America with them. I also wanted to try to make them understand what I was going to do, which, when I thought about it in the cold light of day, was to marry somebody nearly twenty years older than I was, Jewish, a hairdresser who lived in another country, and whom I had known for only a few weeks. I moved back into my own room, waiting for the moment when I would have to discuss my decision with my parents.

I was shy in the face of any kind of confrontation, preferring to let it slide away. I am only now learning how to deal with it, realizing that I have to take care of things myself.

My parents said nothing. I was about to go off to Arizona to do the film and they seemed to feel that if they said nothing about Vidal and me, it would just go away.

When I turned up at the studio with my new look, they were floored, too. Then they decided it was a nice, tough look, just right for the part of a motorcycle moll. We had all arrived at the location in Patagonia, Arizona, when I saw John Cassavetes again. I was sitting in a car and I heard a tap on the window. I looked around and saw it was John. He said, "I'm sorry." He had remembered, too. After that, we were buddies.

It wasn't easy to talk to Vidal from the middle of the Arizona desert, but when I did he kept assuring me that our weeks together hadn't been a dream. As soon as I was back in Los Angeles, he would be on his way.

When the film company returned to Los Angeles, it seemed to me the time had come to sit down with my parents to tell them I really did mean to marry Vidal Sassoon and move to England. Very briefly, they acquiesced. By the time Vidal arrived in Los Angeles, they had changed their minds again.

It wasn't my place to say where Vidal should stay in Los Angeles, but when it turned out that he was going to stay with his old friend, Gene Shacove, who was also a hairdresser, I was jealous. Gene was a notorious ladies' man and I could just see Vidal with the constant stream of beautiful girls who were always in Gene's life.

I was as nervous as I was jealous the day Vidal came to Burbank to meet my parents. He looked incredible in his three-piece suit and his big, fat tie. My father just sat there and fidgeted. My mother wouldn't come out of the bedroom. If there is anything one wants, it is the approval of one's parents. I wasn't even coming close. By the time Vidal left, my mother still hadn't come out of the bedroom. When she did, she underlined her earlier decision. There would be no wedding.

Over the next week, I would drive over the hill to pick up Vidal so that we could go to dinner and talk. There didn't seem to be anything we could do to change my parents' minds. One evening when I got home around midnight, my parents, a neighbor and her daughter were all sitting around talking. It turned out they had been waiting for me. They said they had proof that Vidal was a homosexual. I couldn't believe my ears. The neighbor's daughter said she had met someone who said he had known Vidal in London and that the person was gay. It was ridiculous.

The point of their big whoop-de-doo was to save me. I started an emotional defense of him, complete with dry heaves and tears. By the time it was decided to send me off to stay with my aunt and uncle in Oregon, it was four o'clock in the morning, and I was near collapse. A bag was packed for me, and I was piled into the car to be driven to the airport. When we got there, I called Vidal from a pay phone. I was sobbing and crying and choking. I decided I wasn't going to Oregon. I got back in the car and I begged my parents to take me home. When they realized they were never going to get me on a plane to Oregon or anywhere else, they took me home.

When I woke up the next morning, my girl friend Kathy McElman was there with her mother. I was obviously upset and exhausted. The pair of them took me off to Kathy's apartment. Vidal met me there, and we talked and talked. The only thing to do, we decided, was to get married that day. The only place we could get married that day was Las Vegas.

The ceremony took ninety seconds. I called my parents to tell them we were married. My house was very quiet the next day when I returned to pack my clothes.

Vidal and I went to Puerto Vallarta for our honeymoon. Neither of us knew the other. We had always been surrounded by other people.

Vidal didn't know I didn't like to sit in the sun. He wanted to go water skiing. I didn't want to go water skiing. He wanted to jog. The last thing I was going to do was jog. He liked fresh fruits. I wanted Mexican food. He wanted to take cold showers. Cold showers make my heart stop. When he got up in the morning, he drank lemon juice and hot water. I wanted my nice cup of tea. At the end of our two weeks in Puerto Vallarta, we were beginning to learn how to compromise.

We flew from Puerto Vallarta to Mexico City where we went to all the restaurants and to the spectacular Museum of Anthropology. Then we went on to New York for two weeks. I was in heaven, traveling with fourteen pieces of luggage that held everything I owned. Vidal was very much in the New York social whirl. Through him, I was thrown into it, too. I loved it. When we got on the plane for London two weeks later, all I could think of was that I was going home. Thirty people were waiting for us at Vidal's tiny apartment. Once again the champagne corks popped to celebrate our marriage.

It didn't take too many days before the harsh realization dawned that I had nothing to do. I spent my days opening charge accounts at the meat market, the greengrocer and Harrods, announcing proudly that I was Mrs. Vidal Sassoon.

We found a wonderful two-bedroom apartment across the street from the Carlton Tower on Cadogan Place. The bedroom was barely large enough to get out of bed, but I loved it. I stayed in that wonderful little apartment with the heat on all the time drinking tea, reading all the papers and magazines. I went from shop to shop to market. I loved to read cookbooks and I would make steaks and roasts. Vidal would tell me he was bringing six people home for dinner, and thirty-six would turn up. It all worked out. It was just fine with me. We were often out in the evening for dinner with friends at their homes, at restaurants, at the theater or at parties. On Friday nights, we had that wonderful Jewish food at his parents' house. It was one big cozy year and I loved it.

I would call my parents and write to them. They wouldn't talk to me and they wouldn't answer my letters. The only thing they were hanging onto by that time to hold against Vidal was that he was Jewish. It didn't mean anything at all to me and, in fact, I don't think it made any difference to them, either.

I was amazed at Vidal's discipline. He would jog and he would go to the gym. I was even jealous when he went on his own to the gym. He ate all the heavy foods I cooked, but I think he was just being polite. I was also being polite. I ate bowls of yogurt, wheat germ, raw egg and honey. All I wanted to do was please him. My whole day was spent waiting for him to come home.

I had just settled into my new life when Columbia called. They wanted me to do another Dean Martin film, *Murderer's Row*. It was wonderful to be back in Los Angeles for the week I was shooting there. I didn't see my parents. When I got back to London, I found I was scheduled to do a film in Portugal. It was going to mean that I would be away from Vidal for many weeks, but he promised to visit me. He came for a wonderful, romantic weekend. Vidal and I had talked about having children. Both of us wanted them very much. When I got back from location, I had the idea I might be pregnant.

Indeed I was pregnant. I was so excited when I got the news that I jumped up and down. I was just thrilled. I thought that was the greatest thing ever. So did Vidal when he heard our wonderful news.

He had some news of his own. For some time, Vidal had been thinking about moving to New York. With shops on Bond Street, Sloane Street and in Grovesnor House, he had reached his saturation point in London. He also felt that the big explosion in England was over and that the challenge was in the United States.

The problem was that in England, Vidal was his own boss. In the United States, he wasn't. Charles of the Ritz had bought a third of his name in America, and put up the money for the salon on Madison Avenue. And, even though he had spent a great deal of time in the United States doing hair demonstrations, Vidal didn't have his license and wouldn't be able to work. We had talked and talked about it, and now the decision was made. We were going to move to the United States. Our baby would be born there.

And I was going to be Mrs. Vidal Sassoon of New York.

6

Thoughts About Pregnancy

Creating a new life. Just to think about such a thing makes me catch my breath. What could be more mythic, more magical? But there is a price to be paid. For our own health, the price should be kept as low as possible.

When your doctor confirms that you are pregnant, you will be given a pamphlet explaining what you can expect and how to take care of yourself during the months of pregnancy. While we take care of ourselves, we want to give our babies every possible break.

WHAT NOT TO DO

We know now that even mild social drinking isn't good for the developing fetus. Neither is the caffeine in coffee and tea. Women who smoke deliver babies lower in weight and less healthy than women who don't smoke. It is thought that even aspirin can have adverse effects on a developing fetus.

It is essential that you avoid drinking (whether alcohol, coffee or tea) and smoking, and stay away from aspirin and all other medications unless specifically prescribed by your doctor.

41

NUTRITION

If I ever stuck to a well-balanced nutritional program it was during my pregnancies. The diet I followed consisted of lean meats, fish, lots of fruits and vegetables and dairy products to ensure that my baby and I would be as healthy as possible. Although the national average weight gain during pregnancy is 29 pounds, the developing fetus needs only 500 calories a day. Not only did I want to keep the weight of the baby itself low enough so that it wouldn't have a difficult time being born, but I wanted to keep my own weight in check so that I could get back to my normal shape as soon as possible after the pregnancy.

EXERCISE

Exercising during pregnancy was something I found essential, not only to prevent the loss of muscle tone, but to make the delivery as easy as possible and also to try to prevent stretch marks. Although I went to the gym to keep myself in shape, there are exercises that work just as well that can be done at home. The pamphlet your doctor will give you will list those exercises most beneficial to pregnant women. Swimming and walking are exercises often recommended. For myself, I found that exercises to keep my back stretched and to strengthen my stomach and abdominal muscles were a great help.

Here are two exercises that I particularly recommend:

Back Stretching

1. Lying on the floor with your knees bent and feet slightly apart, grasp one knee and bring it up to your chest. Hold for a count of five, and repeat with your other leg. Your back should be flat against the floor.

2. Lie on the floor with your knees bent and feet slightly apart, your arms outstretched at your sides. With your feet flat against the floor, raise your buttocks and lift your stomach toward the ceiling. (See illustration.) Tighten your buttocks and hold for two seconds. Release and lower yourself to the starting position. Start with 10 repetitions and increase gradually to 25. This will help you during delivery by strengthening your lower back. It also firms your buttocks.

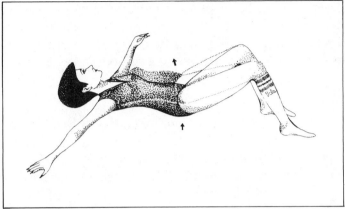

Stretching your back

Strengthening Your Stomach and Abdomen

Lie flat on the floor with your arms straight above your head, your knees bent and feet together. Press your chin onto your chest, curl up slowly, and reach for your outer thigh. (See illustration.) Hold for a count of three and uncurl. Repeat with your other side.

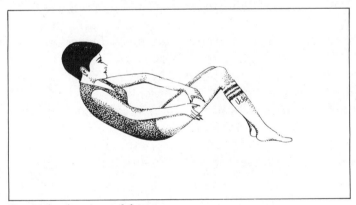

Strengthening your abdomen

HAIR

Pregnancy is a time to pay particular attention to the condition of your hair so that it won't look lank and lifeless. A protein conditioner might be added to your usual shampooing and conditioning program. It might be the time for a new haircut, or a henna rinse to add highlights to your hair.

Some women experience hair loss during pregnancy and for

several months after the baby is delivered. This hair loss can be caused by an increased amount of the hormone progesterone in the system. As the level of progesterone returns to normal, the hair will start to grow back, sometimes more luxuriantly than before.

SKIN

Many women find they have never looked as radiant as they do when they are pregnant. Others find themselves with skin problems they've never had before. Because of an increased amount of the hormone estrogen in the first four months, your skin may be dry. This condition can be brought into balance by following the skin care program for dry skin outlined in my morning routine (p. 12). During the third trimester, there is an increased amount of the hormone progesterone in the body. Skin that was dry earlier in pregnancy will now either balance itself or become oily. If it does become oily, it can be brought into balance by following the skin care program for oily skin outlined in the morning routine (p. 12).

One of the objections that I have to all of the fad diets that come and go is that sudden weight loss plays havoc with the skin. There is no more sudden weight loss than delivering a baby, and that can result in diminished muscle tone and stretch marks, which are caused when the skin is stretched beyond its elastic ability. The result of such stretching is fine red or violet lines, usually found on the abdomen, breasts and thighs. These lines will lose their pigment after delivery, leaving fine whitish lines.

I didn't want stretch marks, and so I kept my body lubricated all the time with a Vitamin E oil or Aloe Vera. It is available at drugstores and health food stores. I can't guarantee that you won't have stretch marks if you use it, but it did work for me.

TEETH

It is important to visit your dentist as soon as you learn you are pregnant. The developing fetus is going to take the calcium it needs from your system, and making certain your teeth and gums are in good condition is a necessity. Milk and dairy products are high in calcium and excellent sources for the added calcium you are going to need.

HANDS AND FEET

Water retention (or edema) during pregnancy is most noticeable when you get up in the morning, or when you've been sitting for long periods of time. This edema is minimized during the course of the day as you move around. To help get your circulation going and to diminish the edema, I suggest that you elevate on the balls of your feet several times in the morning and in the afternoon. Edema in the hands can be diminished by shaking them out several times during the day. Some doctors recommend taking water pills to control edema during pregnancy and if it is a major problem, I would suggest asking your doctor.

Remember that paying particular attention to your manicure and pedicure can give you a needed psychological lift.

FATIGUE

While I was pregnant, I made it a priority to avoid fatigue. I got my eight hours sleep each night and scheduled ten-minute periods at regular intervals during the day when I could lie down, or at least put my feet up. If you spend your day at a desk, it would be a good idea to keep your feet elevated on a stool. Get up from your desk every half hour and walk around. Try to walk during your lunch hours or your coffee breaks. Increasing your circulation will diminish fatigue.

MAKEUP

Even if you can't entirely avoid fatigue, at least you don't have to let it show. Take particular care with your eye makeup for a wide-open, sparkling look. A little more blusher than usual will give your face a rosy glow that isn't there naturally.

With proper nutrition, exercise, hair and skin care, rest and these few little psychological pickups, it is possible to keep your own health at a peak, and to assure the delivery of a baby who is as healthy as it can possibly be.

7

Mrs. Vidal Sassoon of New York

When we moved to New York in the spring of 1968, things were so tight financially that we were living in one room in the Regency Hotel. In London, everything was put right back into the company; in New York, Vidal could take a salary from only one salon.

We found an apartment with a lovely view of the city on the twenty-second floor of a building on 60th Street between Park and Lexington avenues. There was an L-shaped living room, a tiny kitchen, a bath, and two bedrooms. Of course, we had no furniture at all, and when we went out in the evening, we were never able to invite anybody back.

In the health and beauty business, or in any other business, it is important to exude confidence and to look prosperous. I invested in one clingy, black dress for evenings and I wore it with different shawls to give it a variety of looks.

Vidal was working with Redken Products, touring the country doing shows for hairdressers in order to buy back his name and the salon on Madison Avenue from Charles of the Ritz. We had no money, but it didn't matter; everything was fun and romantic and exciting. I loved being pregnant, and Vidal loved it, too.

The social life in New York was easy. All I had to do was look good. If I didn't agree with what was being said, I didn't say anything. I was still unsure of myself, still intimidated. In those early years in New York I met a number of people who are still among my closest friends. And, with a grandchild on its way, my parents came around at last.

I made up my mind that I was going to be a lady about the actual delivery. I was not going to shout, scream or cry, and I was going to be awake. In talking over my requirements with my doctor, I found that I could have the delivery I wanted with an epidural. It is an injection into the sheath surrounding the spinal column. The effect is rather like a shot of Novocain from the waist down.

I had invited my mother to make her first trip to New York for the birth of her grandchild. Because the doctor was going to induce labor, I knew exactly what my schedule would be. The night before the baby was to be born, I got up after dinner, washed and set my hair, and went to bed. In the morning, I carefully put on my makeup and my false eyelashes. Vidal was standing in front of the closet in the bedroom. "I've never been a father before," he said. "I don't know what to wear."

When we finally got everybody together, we went off in a taxi to Mount Sinai. They put me in this little room, and I had the humbling experiences of an enema and being shaved. Vidal stayed with me. He was trying to be very calm and he had an amiable chat with the doctor about the cultural life of New York. I was given an intravenous injection, the anesthetist rolled me over on my side, and the epidural was administered. I started to feel less comfortable. In the rooms around me, all the women were screaming. They broke the water, and then it really started to hurt.

I was wheeled into the delivery room, and out popped this little creature—the daughter I had hoped for! I was laughing and crying at the same time. From the moment I walked in through the front door of the hospital it had taken only two hours. The biggest thing after that was getting out of bed the first time and walking down the hall to the nursery. There were thirty screaming babies, but I could tell which was my own Catya.

It was the right time in my life for me to be a wife and mother, although I never looked upon any point in my life as a last and final move, nor do I now. As I developed as a person, I was starting to feel more secure. I loved being with Catya and couldn't wait until she started to talk so that I could tell her about trees and animals, about all of that great, big world out there. I certainly didn't look like anybody's idea of a beauty expert then. I was fat, and there were circles under my eyes.

My life was the baby and the market. Shopping for clothes in New York was easy. The only place I ever went was Lady Madonna. There were always fresh flowers all over the apartment. I experimented with recipes. I prepared different fish dishes, roasts, and chicken, which is high in protein and low in fat. I cleaned cupboards, and I did the laundry. I did have the luxury of going to the salon to get my hair and nails done. In the evening, Vidal and I were usually out. I was learning how to organize my time between Vidal, the baby, the apartment and looking after myself as well.

When I found out that I was pregnant again, it was clear we were going to have to move. I found a three-bedroom apartment a few blocks away, and we moved in just before Elan was born.

When I went back into the hospital it was to the same little room at Mount Sinai. I had been gone only a little more than a year. This time, Vidal sat with me and read a book—upside down. Our son, Elan, was born on his father's birthday.

Now that we were parents, the quality of the time Vidal and I spent together changed. The romantic time one spends with one's husband is certainly different when it is punctuated by little cries from the nursery. With two tiny babies, it was very important for me to get my proper rest at night, and I did some serious sleeping.

Things were still very tight in terms of the business. One month, Vidal didn't have enough money for the payment to Charles of the Ritz. I called my mother and had her send me all the savings bonds I had accumulated during my adolescence and when I was acting. It wasn't much, but it kept the business going for another quarter.

With his strong confidence, Vidal was always convinced everything was going to be just fine. He would send me flowers and buy me gifts I knew were too extravagant. There were no picket fences in New York, but our marriage and our children were a nice, compact little package that suited both of us. I did everything I could to please my husband. I dressed to please him and I ate what he thought I should. If I thought of myself at all, it was still as a nice accessory to somebody else's life.

Every weekend we would take the babies and go to the park and the museums. Though they were tiny, we felt they would absorb what they were seeing and be more receptive when they were older. After they started nursery school at Dalton, I would fix them each a little piece of fresh filet of sole and fresh vegetables as a snack when they got home. They were too young to fight me, so they ate what was right. They would sit in their high chairs and eat their fish and vegetables like little angels. Of course, later when they found out about junk food they joined right in. Vidal and I spent years worrying that they were going to eat garbage forever. Now I see them in restaurants ordering salads and vegetables.

There were always business meetings in the apartment. A group of associates was forming Vidal Sassoon, Inc. We talked about the business night and day. In exchange for one-eighth of the new company, an investment group in England bought out Charles of the Ritz's interest in Vidal. What a relief it was when that obligation was finally over.

A Vidal Sassoon salon had opened successfully in Toronto. The first barber shop had been opened in connection with the beauty salon on Sloane Street in London, although it wasn't possible to open one in connection with the beauty salon in New York because of state laws regarding separate entrances for men and women.

Acceptance of the barber shop was very slow. Artists, actors, photographers, restaurateurs, men who are aware of how they look all responded favorably, but, for the most part, men felt like sissies having their hair cut and styled. It embarrassed them to have it blow dried, or to sit under the dryer with their hair in a net. Basically, Vidal's idea was that hair has no sex in the sense that geometry should be used to cut the hair according to the bone structure of the face. If there is a choice between having your hair cut so that it will look good and suit you instead of looking bad, why not look good? He always felt the time would come when men would be concerned about how they looked, and he was right.

It was decided that the next salon should be opened in Beverly Hills. In 1970, a huge party was held in a tented-off parking lot to celebrate the opening. Five hundred people, many of them celebrities, came to the party. The live music blared, the food was marvelous, the congratulations were effusive. There weren't enough scrapbooks to hold all the clips that poured in when it was over. There was only one problem: After the party, there were no clients. The stylists sat in the back room for months on end playing gin rummy. There was nothing else for them to do. When Vidal was on the scene, business would pick up, then it would drop off again.

Joe Solomon, president of Vidal Sassoon, Inc., had started as a shampoo boy in the New York salon. Then he became a stylist. He was head of the new Beverly Hills salon. Neither he nor anybody else could figure out what was wrong. It was agony. Toronto was a success. New York was a success. London was a success.

In those cities, people would stand in front of the windows watching the stylists doing haircuts the way they used to look at television in store windows when it first came out. And it wasn't as if the people in Beverly Hills were frightened of innovation. Hairdressers like Carrie White and Hugh York had vast followings. One of the problems was that the salon was on the second floor, which meant there was no hope for foot traffic. It was thought that it might be a good idea to close it up. All sorts of people were brought in to run a wig and clothing boutique. What it was going to take was word of mouth and it was a long time before it was certain that the Beverly Hills salon would survive.

On one of our visits to England, English *Cosmopolitan* did a piece on Vidal. There were several pictures of him with me and the children. When the spread came out, I learned that he had posed for a nude centerfold. I was at a dinner party with some friends the night he came back from London with an issue of the magazine. He brought it along on the assumption, I suppose, that I wouldn't show my rage in front of our friends. Vidal's rationale was that it showed a forty-year-old man who was in terrific shape and that it was good in terms of the health and beauty programs in which he believed. It seemed to me that it lessened the prestige he had worked so hard to build up. And I felt really betrayed and hurt: He hadn't even trusted me enough to ask what I thought. I was so angry that my whole body was affected, so hurt that I could barely see. It was the beginning of a loss of respect for him and it made me realize, for the first time, that I wasn't just this little person who would go along with anything. I had my first doubts about our relationship and the way we communicated.

I spent a lot of time that summer in Southhampton doing some serious soul-searching. I had looked for a house to rent in May, found one, and organized our move there. On the surface, the summer was spent lying in the sun and playing with the kids, entertaining our friends. But I knew something was wrong. A seed had been planted.

Another problem was my desire to be involved with something other than the business. We talked about the business day and night. While it was true that the business was paying for the way we lived and we were having a lot of fun, I was beginning to think about doing something for myself, for Beverly.

But what would it be? I didn't have the education to do anything. I was limited in terms of the commercials I could do because I was so identified with Vidal. I remember one evening when Vidal and I took a walk along the beach in Southhampton. I told him I didn't want him to misunderstand, but underneath somewhere there was a Beverly and I could feel her trying to come out.

I rationalized that perhaps because Vidal was traveling so much, I was feeling left out because I was tied down with the children. And if I was feeling left out, I had to find something to do within the limitations of caring for the children. I did know that I wasn't being challenged at all.

The one thing I had done earlier in the year was to take some classes in interior design. I didn't want to be an interior designer, but I did want to know about antiques and different periods. I enjoyed the classes and I found out I had certain skills in learning.

By the time we returned to New York in the fall, I had decided nothing. If I threw my energies into interior design or some other field totally different from Vidal's, there was the question of whether I would be successful. Perhaps the answer was simply to go on as we were. We would go through periods where we were communicating perfectly and I would be content. I had been wrong, I would tell myself. We were as happy as we had ever been. But doubts kept coming to the surface of my mind. Here we were, this wonderful couple, and I didn't know why that didn't satisfy me anymore. I was anxious about my feelings and I didn't understand them.

Vidal was in Texas doing a talk show. The children and I were going to join him for a few days at a condominium which belonged to friends at the Palm Bay Club in Florida. The night before we were to leave, I stayed up very late talking about my feelings with my friend, Elaine.

I don't remember ever having been so tired, so confused, and so frightened of my feelings when I got on the airplane the next morning with the children and their nurse. We were barely in the air before I realized I was going to be sick. I rushed to the bathroom. In a few minutes, I knew I was going to be sick again. I took one of the kids along because I had just been in the bathroom. After that, I didn't care anymore. I started to feel dizzy and faint. There was a pulling across my eyes and it was hard for me to see. My mouth was numb, and I had a tingling sensation in my hands and feet. I tried to explain to the stewardess what was happening to me, but I couldn't speak. I couldn't control one of my eyes. It got so bad that my hands and feet went into spasms. They put me on the floor and they took off my boots. My children were carried screaming to the back of the plane. I thought that I was having a heart attack or an epileptic seizure. My greatest fear was that if I passed out I would die.

Nothing was working. A doctor on the plane decided I should have a tube of oxygen up each of my nostrils. A wonderful man who was a retired ophthalmologist sat with me, talking and talking. He talked about football games he had seen, the weather, anything to calm me down. Everybody on the plane suddenly had to go to the bathroom so they could look at me. Those were the longest hours in my life.

When we landed, two men came on the plane. They wrapped me in a sheet and put me on a stretcher. I ended up in the hospital.

By the time Vidal arrived in Miami, friends had insisted I be moved to the Miami Heart Institute where they knew several doctors. By the time I was put back into the ambulance to make the trip to the Miami Heart Institute, I could speak, but I was so weak I could barely raise my arm.

Every imaginable test was run on me. Nothing was wrong. They loaded me down with Valium and Composine. I was so weak and euphoric by the time I got back to the Palm Bay Club that I didn't care about anything.

Vidal thought it would be a good idea for me to have a complete rest. He took the children and their nurse and went home. After they left, my hardest decision each day was which bikini to wear while I lay in the sun. It was about all I could handle. Sandy Staub, a good friend and talented jewelry designer, stayed on to keep me company. I was experiencing a new sense of freedom just being able to have lunch or dinner with her with no demands on me. I ran into somebody I had dated very casually in California before my marriage. He took me to the races and to dinner. In an odd way, the attention he paid an old friend was an affirmation of my own separateness. I stopped taking the tranquilizers. By the time I got back to New York, all the symptoms of what had been an anxiety attack were gone. I was quite myself again—which meant that all the doubts I had taken with me to Florida were still intact.

Vidal was totally supportive of anything I wanted to do. He was always talking to people about my days in films and the commercials I had done. Now that I wanted to reach out, he was as supportive as he always was. I was the problem. I was like a horse at the gate, but I not only didn't know what the track was going to be like, I didn't even know what race I was in. Even though it was only a decade ago, women didn't have the strong feelings of independence they have now. I felt that I had no right to the feelings I was having, and I felt guilty. I knew I was beginning to have opinions, but I wasn't sure what they were.

Like so many women faced with an insolvable quandary, I got pregnant. It seemed like a good omen. I was as excited as if the pregnancy were my first. At the dentist's office when I was two months' pregnant, I began to hemorrhage. There was blood everywhere. My dentist went with me in the taxi to my obstetrician's office and on the way I realized I didn't care if I lost the baby. I already had my two children. My life was a maze of problems. If this pregnancy were fated not to be, then that would be something I would live with.

The obstetrician managed to control my bleeding and I was sent home. He told me I was to do nothing. I couldn't even exercise. Vidal took the children to London for Christmas. After a couple of days at home, I felt well enough to join them.

When I had my first anxiety attack, I didn't want to be told it was psychological. That thought was totally unacceptable to me. I wanted it to be something physical, like a calcium deficiency that could be corrected. In London, I awoke one morning with another anxiety attack. I was throwing up and my hands and feet were like claws. Although this second anxiety attack was nowhere near as bad as the first, I still went to bed to rest and relax. And I had an excuse this time. Anxiety attacks sometimes accompany pregnancy.

When we returned to New York, I was less and less interested in any kind of social life. I was gaining an enormous amount of weight. I was huge, feeling ugly, and very depressed. I was too embarrassed to even walk down the street. When we would go to a restaurant, I wouldn't be able to focus on a conversation. I was so restless that I would have to get up and leave. I was thinking all the time, but I didn't quite know about what. What I did know was that I was tearing myself apart. I don't know how Vidal took it.

Still, anxiety can be profitable. A lot of people will have those feelings and compound them with guilt. The real question is how to take the negative parts of life, learn from them, and turn them into positive experiences. I didn't figure that out until later.

Summer was approaching, and once again I went to Southhampton to find a house to rent. Once I had gotten my family, my mother, and Vidal's mother, settled in, I went back to New York to wait for my baby to be born. Because of my history of quick deliveries my obstetrician didn't want me to be too far away from the hospital.

New York was hot, sticky and muggy. All Vidal and I did was go to the theater or to the movies. I was so uncomfortable and fed up that I decided what I was feeling must be labor pains. I felt like a blob because I had gained forty pounds. My legs were like tree trunks. I couldn't sleep no matter how I propped up various parts of myself with pillows. My own doctor was on vacation and the doctor who was covering for him didn't know me. I thought I could convince him that I really was having labor pains. I marched myself in twice more. He sent me home both times. Every time I left the house I would rush to the hospital immediately.

Finally, the doctor agreed to induce labor and back I went to the same labor room at Mount Sinai. Vidal wanted to be in the delivery room this time to see our child born. After I went into the labor room, he and the doctor went down the hall to change into hospital greens. Nobody was in the room with me except a woman who was cleaning the walls. I asked her if she would mind finding a nurse. When the nurse walked in, she said, ''Oh, my God. The baby's head is showing.'' She and another nurse wheeled me down the hall. The doctor, with Vidal at his heels, came flying through the door of the delivery room. Within forty-five seconds Eden was born. All Vidal could say was, ''Oh, wow.'' He said it over and over.

Eden was a tiny baby. She weighed just under four pounds. The placenta had ruptured, and she was underweight and jaundiced. She spent two weeks in an incubator with her eyes bandaged and tubes inserted into her skull. It broke my heart to look at her. Finally, she weighed enough so that I could hold her to give her a bottle.

It was anticlimactic to go out to Southhampton to visit the troops without the baby. And troops was the right word. Our friends, Ann and Tom Yeardye, were there with their two young children and their new baby who had been born a few days before Eden. Friends from England were there. The mothers were there. When Eden was finally able to leave the hospital, they handed her to me in a little cardboard box. My mother and I drove out to Southhampton while Eden slept contentedly in her box.

I was determined to get back in shape. Using the techniques developed by a Russian dancer, Lotte Berk, which had been franchised to a woman named Lydia Bach, who ran an exercise studio in Southhampton, I started working out there every day. I was so big and so bloated that I wouldn't be seen wearing a swimsuit. It took me eight weeks of constant exercise and watching my diet before I was back to normal. I still do some of the exercises based on those methods.

Those months when I lived on fresh fruit and vegetables were wonderful. I had my own little health farm going. Just after I gave birth to Catya, you could say hello to me and I would burst into tears. Now, my mood was fabulous. I was busy and active. I was so busy with the two little children, with the new baby, with the relatives and the houseguests that I had no time for the postpartum depression I had had twice before. We gave an incredible party at the end of the summer. The highlight for me was that I could actually fit into a wonderful white silk shirt and a pair of size eight, gray trousers.

When Vidal had to go off on a business trip while we were still in Southhampton, I was sitting on top of the world. Some of the houseguests and I were going to a party at the home of friends who lived nearby. We went zipping over and as I walked in through the front door, I had another anxiety attack. I walked right past the host and out the back door where I sat down on my hands to control their spasms. My houseguests rushed me home. I was trying to relax but I was gasping, hyperventilating, and I couldn't stop. I ended up in the hospital with an injection to calm me down. I went home to bed and I stayed there. While trying to lose weight and deal with the kids, the new baby, the relatives and the houseguests, I had done too much. I pulled myself up short and curtailed my activities as much as I could. It was time to take care of me.

When I was pregnant with Eden, there had been talk of our doing a book. Because of the television appearances I had made with Vidal, it seemed a good idea to have us do the book as a husband and wife team. Shortly after Eden was born, we began to work on *A Year of Beauty and Health.*

The corporate offices of Vidal Sassoon, Inc., were now a small cluster in a building in Century City in Los Angeles. We were going to move to California, which wasn't going to be a gigantic step forward from a financial point of view. Every house we looked at was totally beyond our reach. The ones in our price range were a mess. Sometimes on Sundays when I was a kid in Burbank, my parents and I would drive to Beverly Hills to look at all the big houses. I still remembered one of the houses the real estate person showed me from those Sunday drives so many years ago.

After all those years of living in apartments, first in London and then in New York, the house in Beverly Hills was so big by comparison that it looked like a palace. Everything needed doing; there wasn't even a bathroom for the master bedroom. I fell in love with it at once. When Vidal came to see it with me, he fell in love with it, too.

Then I was really nervous about moving. California isn't like New York where you can walk out the front door and become a part of the life of the city. In California, you have to make your own life. I knew the only way I could survive was to start to do things on my own instead of just thinking about them. There would be no more conjecture, no more endless weighing of options. It was time to start to become Beverly Sassoon of Beverly Hills.

8

Your Special Needs As a New Mother

During pregnancy, there is all the fun of preparing for the arrival of the baby, thinking of names, buying the layette, painting the nursery, stocking up with nursery paraphernalia, such as bottles and bottle brushes, cans of formula, boxes of disposable diapers and little jars of baby food. There is also the fact that this pleasant stage of anticipation takes place over a period of nine months. The stages of pregnancy occur gradually, almost unnoticeably, until it is time for the actual birth.

When the new mother returns to her room in the hospital, she is greeted with flowers and cards, with delighted calls from friends and relatives. The baby arrives for its feedings and then is taken away to the nursery, allowing the new mother to get plenty of rest, and to quietly savor her accomplishment.

The first few days at home are exciting, too. There are the visits from friends, the gifts, and solicitude and pampering from husband, friends and relatives, the fact that in the next room is the baby who has been the center of your fantasies for so many months, living and breathing, the personification of hope.

While the months of pregnancy give the prospective mother time to get used to the idea of a baby, the birth itself is very abrupt. One minute there is the thought of a baby, and the next minute there is the baby itself, with its incessant needs. I have never heard of a prospective mother who was really prepared for the fact that a baby is always there. I certainly wasn't. Intellectually I understood that when I brought Catya home from the hospital she would always be there, but emotionally I didn't grasp, until I was faced with it, that for at least awhile what mattered were her needs—mine didn't count at all. And a new baby's needs are totally random. The only thing I found I could count on was that Catya would start to cry if I had just put dinner on the table, or if I had just sat down with a book and put my feet up.

I found that I would burst into tears for no reason at all, and I tried to keep firmly in my mind the fact that it was going to take some time for my hormonal system to return to its usual balance. I had lost quite a bit of weight at her birth, but my stomach muscles were still flaccid and, looking at myself in the mirror, it seemed I would never have the firm, supple body I was used to seeing.

Because of the many abrupt changes I realized my body was undergoing after Catya's birth, I knew it was no time to start to play Wonder Woman. Still, through experimenting, I found there were some techniques that helped to bring my body and psychological state back to normal.

BE SELFISH ABOUT GETTING YOUR REST

I did a lot of sleeping when my babies were tiny because my body needed it. When the babies had their naps, I had a nap, too, even though I often was interrupted in the middle of it. When I went to bed at night, I tried not to keep an ear cocked toward the nursery. I consciously concentrated on pastoral scenes or a festive dinner I wanted to prepare. I would count slowly backward from a hundred, willing away the tension that had accumulated during the day as I tried to anticipate the unanticipatable needs of a new baby. Often, Vidal would respond to the nighttime calls. While it was true that he was tired from a day at the salon, it was my body and not his that was recovering from birth. Don't feel guilty about asking your husband or others to help you. By getting your proper rest, you are speeding the day when you will be your pre-pregnancy self again.

NUTRITION

Most women take on additional fat stores during pregnancy. To mobilize this fat after the baby is born, you should keep the fats and carbohydrates in your diet to a minimum. Choose instead a diet high in proteins, which should include lean meats, fish, poultry, eggs and foods from the dairy groups.

Remember to eat your fruits and vegetables each day. Citrus fruits, such as oranges and grapefruits, are good sources of Vitamin A and Vitamin C. Cantaloupe, strawberries, broccoli, and green and red peppers are other good sources of Vitamin C. Dark green and yellow vegetables are sources of Vitamin A. Because of the added iron requirements during pregnancy, foods rich in this mineral should be emphasized. The main food sources for iron are meats, especially organ meats, such as liver and kidneys, shellfish, eggs, leafy dark green vegetables, whole grain or enriched breads, cereals and dried fruits. You might want to ask your doctor if you need an iron tablet.

Be relaxed about your diet, but when you feel up to it take a personal inventory and work out a plan. It is not the time to go on a crash diet because you need all the essential basic foods to build yourself up. If you still retain a lot of fluid in your tissues and your hands and feet seem puffy to you, this is not the time to take a diuretic. The fluid will redistribute itself in about six weeks and be excreted naturally as your hormone level returns to normal. You might also limit the salt in your diet. Artichokes and cucumbers are both natural diuretics. The caffeine in coffee is also a natural diuretic.

BODY SHAPE

Exercise is one of the quickest ways to get your body in shape again, but during the first weeks after your baby's birth, it is wise to restrict what you do. If possible, let somebody else take care of the housework for the first week and devote your energy to establishing a relationship with your baby. During the first four weeks after your baby is born, your abdominal muscles are returning to their original lengths, and your uterus is shrinking back to its usual size. The pamphlet your doctor has given you will outline a few simple exercises you can do almost immediately after your baby is born. Four weeks after the birth, you can gradually get back to the stretches, warm-ups and spot exercises outlined in the section on how you can have the very best body shape it is possible for you to have.

I think the most important thing to remember during the early days of motherhood is that your strength is at a premium. Be selfish—be as easy on yourself as you can be.

HAIR

As soon as you can, make an appointment with your stylist and have your hair cut. Perhaps you might also want to cheer yourself up with a temporary color rinse to give your hair some highlights. In the early postpartum days, the hair you have lost during pregnancy has yet to reappear. A temporary color rinse and a good haircut will cheer you up.

HANDS AND FEET

A manicure and a pedicure, either performed professionally, or by you at home will cheer you up, too. There is something about well-cared for hands and feet that will make you feel as if you're part of that big world out there that doesn't just have to do with dirty diapers and being on constant call to your little prince or princess.

MAKEUP

I think the most common problem most women have after giving birth is fatigue, which usually results in pallor and dark circles under the eyes. Remember the cardinal rule of ''no makeup'' makeup. Don't try to lighten the dark circles under your eyes with a lighter foundation. This will only emphasize them. Instead, use your usual shade, or even one that is slightly darker. And don't forget the miracle of subtly applied blusher. You may as well have a rosy glow, no matter how deceptive it is!

BE SELFISH ABOUT YOUR TIME ALONE

Whenever somebody offers to look after the baby, take them up on it. As soon as you can, begin your search for competent baby-sitters, and use them. At some point in the delivery room, the umbilical cord that linked your baby to you was cut. At that point, even though the baby is totally dependent, you are officially two separate people. Don't feel guilty about reaffirming this fact. Even if it's only for ten minutes, take that time and go for a walk. You have had a baby, but being a mother is not your only role. You are still you, a separate, functioning individual with needs of your own.

BE SELFISH ABOUT YOUR TIME WITH YOUR HUSBAND

Remember when the two of you fell in love? Those candlelight dinners, the champagne, the jogging together, or the sailing, the realization of that wonderful whatever-it-is that draws two people together and turns them into a couple? After your baby is born, you are not only still a separate individual, but you are also still the wife and lover of the man you love and chose to marry. Value your romantic time together.

As soon as you can, the two of you should plan a romantic outing together, whether it is a walk on the beach or dinner in a favorite restaurant. There is something about dressing up and going out to dinner with the man you love that seems to be the first step along the path toward feeling attractive, feminine, and as desirable as you always were.

When a baby is small, it is totally dependent. At that point, motherhood is more demanding than anything else a woman undertakes. Motherhood, though, is only one facet of a woman's life. We are also wives and lovers, daughters and friends, neighbors and career women. Don't feel guilty about the time it takes to fulfill the other facets of your life.

WHEN YOUR CHILD IS OLDER

So much of what we eat is for emotional satisfaction rather than nutrition that early childhood is the time to introduce into your child's diet foods that will fulfill both emotional and nutritional needs. In short, food to a young child represents love, and it might as well be the right food. Keep cookies, candy and all junk foods out of the house. Fruits and vegetables are high-energy snacks and eating them instead of an afternoon cookie will be better nutritionally for your child, and will also establish habits that will outlast the junk food he or she will discover later.

Encourage your child to exercise along with you. This will also establish patterns essential in the child's attitude toward taking care of herself later. Try to get in a daily walk, taking your child along. Walking is unsurpassed for building and maintaining endurance. I think we must remember that we are the primary role models in the lives of our children.

9

Beverly Sassoon of Beverly Hills— Part I

It was pouring the day we moved into our new home, inside as well as out. Within days, the electricians, carpenters and contractors descended on us. In the midst of chaos, we were working on our book. In those first days of writing the book, the two of us worked together with the writer. Soon it became apparent that when Vidal was talking and I was just sitting there, and vice versa, it was a waste of time. We started to alternate, and these separate sessions led to an interesting insight. Vidal's approach to beauty and health was far more rigid than mine. My own approach was far more pragmatic and certainly a lot more fun.

Nobody can be perfect. I know I'm not. Around the time *A Year of Beauty and Health* came out, my kids wanted to go to McDonald's one day. As any mother knows, if you have four kids, sometimes you have eight in tow, and sometimes you have twelve. I was there in my jeans and my T-shirt with all these kids tugging at me, all of them wanting this or wanting that. The tray I was carrying was loaded down with Big Macs, milk shakes, malts and French fries. Somebody came up to me and asked in an amazed voice if I hadn't just written a book about beauty and health. There I stood with a tray full of junk food. Well, why not? Why couldn't I be at McDonald's like everybody else? The point is to have a self-care program that is a pleasure, not a pain. I allow myself a day at McDonald's, but the next day I compensate for it.

Vidal was away for seven months that first year. I was happy to stay home. I was there to get the house together and to attend to the children. They were small enough so that they adjusted to California as if they had never known another home. They immediately started to make friends, many of whom are still in their lives. I think a couple of them came with the mortgage. Catya started first grade and Elan was going to a little nursery school. The baby, of course, was still at home.

I saw my old friends from high school. I started to make new friends. When Vidal was home, we were whooshed into the social whirl. The house was far from finished but it was in working order. I decided it was time to do something for myself. I hated to admit it, but I was bored.

I wanted to go to school. I didn't know what I wanted to do when I got there, but I hoped I would find out. I decided to enroll in a community college instead of starting right off at UCLA.

There was something else on my mind. When Vidal and I were newly married in London, it was the time of the Bangladesh war. We had wanted to adopt a war orphan but the red tape made it impossible for us. One night, at a dinner party, I was talking to a woman who had just had a second baby of the same sex as her first. She said she was going to try again. I asked her why she didn't adopt. She said it was a problem because you couldn't get a child who would fit into the family. I said that I understood that older children were available, or children of different colors or nationalities. She was shocked, and literally said, "But what would the neighbors think?"

Then I listened to myself. Here I was proposing something I hadn't done anything about myself. The next morning I called the Los Angeles County Department of Adoptions to ask about the procedure. When Vidal came home from work, I asked him what he thought about it. Because of the years he had spent in a London orphanage, he had always wanted to help somebody else. He asked me if I really wanted to do it, pointing out that Eden was barely old enough to walk. I said yes and he agreed enthusiastically.

When Vidal and I went to our first meeting, we knew the child we would be permitted to adopt would be a mixed child, which was fine with both of us. With your own children, I think you want to see what you can create. Now we were able to think about some of those children out there who didn't have the opportunities our own children had, the children who wouldn't be able to get an education, who didn't have relationships with parents and siblings.

My own children had been exposed to people from all races and from all walks of life. Although it may be terribly romantic and idealistic of me, I don't think that children see people in different colors. I was concerned about what a new child in the family would do to the children, but I wasn't afraid. After all, they had parents who traveled a lot, who were always saying hello and good-bye. They were flexible and hearty.

We decided that we wanted an older boy, one who wouldn't take either the role of the oldest child in the family, or the role of the baby. We wanted a child who would fit in somewhere among our own.

The Los Angeles County Department of Adoptions was already trying to find a child for us when I went out to buy my notebooks, my pens and all the other paraphernalia that goes along with school. I felt just like a little kid.

I had decided to start slowly. There were the children, the house, and I was still going to have to travel. Because Santa Monica City College is on the semester system, it wouldn't be too drastic if I had to be away for a few days. I didn't even know what the word sociology meant until I went in to register, but I signed up for Sociology I. I also signed up for a child development class offered in the psychology department.

At first, I felt totally out of place. There were the real young kids straight out of high school and the older students. At twenty-eight, I was in the middle. I used to park my Mercedes blocks away and walk to the campus. Around the house, I was already beginning to rebel against having to look perfect all the time. I wore a scarf over my hair all the time—the neighbors didn't know I was a brunette. Now that I was in school, I loved being anonymous.

The child development class was a snap. It was wonderful in theory, but nothing I could put into practice at home! Sociology was opening up a whole new world for me. There were things I was reading about for the first time. All I could think of was what I had been missing until now.

Going to college had other benefits for me. It made me feel accepted in an area other than the one with which I was so identified. Nobody ever said, "Are you Beverly Sassoon?" It was an atmosphere that was good for me and my growth.

The summer I had taken on more difficult classes, the book came out. Friends took notes for me in my classes, while Vidal and

I traveled around the country to promote the book. We were constantly on radio and television and there were dozens of printed interviews. My comfortable anonymity at school was gone.

When we started to tour, I was relieved to discover it was going to be nothing like the tours I did as a little starlet in a bubble bath. Now I was regarded as an individual. People in all areas were treating me as an equal. This made me feel different about myself and I know I acted differently as I became more credible to other people.

The interviews we gave were about hair, bone structure, makeup, health and exercise. I ran around the country doing my little party tricks. I was always in leotards with boots and a skirt over them. I made more changes than Wonder Woman. Because there usually wasn't time for me to do my warm-up exercises before an appearance, I was always limping out of television studios because I pulled muscles and ligaments. When we were in Los Angeles, I rushed back to school. As I pulled into the parking lot one day and jumped out of the car, I found that I had forgotten my books. When I leaned back into the car to get them, the door swung back and hit me. Within an hour my vision was blurred and I felt weak and peculiar. I left class and went to the doctor. He told me I had a slight concussion and whiplash.

At around the same time, Vidal did a breakfast for three hundred women in a department store. He came down a T-runway, missed a step, and fell five feet. He recovered nicely with the remark, ''I've never fallen for so many beautiful women at one time.'' The next thing I heard was that he was all taped and bandaged. Off we went to do our tour about health and beauty with his tapes and bandages and my neck brace. It was so painful. At night we would argue over who got the heating pad.

Vidal called home every night to speak to the kids, but I had such feelings of guilt about being away from them that sometimes I couldn't even speak to them. When I did, all I would hear was, ''Mom, when are you coming home?'' So it was guilt when I spoke to them and more guilt when I didn't. We are so programmed, so socialized to believe that it is okay for Daddy to be working during the day and only available between dinner and bedtime that the transition to the father away on business is not that difficult to make. The woman, on the other hand, is either in the home most of the time or she is expected to be.

Women I speak with on my lecture tours feel resentment that they can't be comfortable at home with their kids where they ''should'' be. They say they are bored, and that they resent the situation and their children. Then they get out and enter the world, and they develop the guilts out there. They say, ''Gee, I'm enjoying it, but I should be at home.'' They lose either way.

I think a balance can be struck. I really hope what matters is the quality of time you spend with your children. More and more children are being brought up with working mothers, single mothers, or they see friends of their mothers who work. The change in attitude has to come from the women. I think if a mother can come to grips with the situation, it will be acceptable for her to go out and be a person. She has to get to the point where it isn't taking away from her role as a mother to be working and she has to feel comfortable with that. If she feels it is all right for her to be working, her attitude will filter to the children. *They* will accept it as a matter of course if *she* does.

In generations past, there was the notion that if a woman wasn't with her children for twenty-four hours a day it was going to ruin their lives. But each child is a combination of environment and genetics, and most of them are more resilient than we give them credit for. Many of us have to hope so, anyway, especially those of us who have to work either for financial reasons or for our own sense of ourselves.

It was on the book tour that I felt as if I were really involved for the first time. Vidal and I had little routines worked out. He would say a certain word and I would jump in. When I would say a certain word he would jump in.

When we would finally get to our hotel room in the evening, I would be sitting there and taking all the stuff off my face and all of the bottles on the table would be jumping around because Vidal was jumping rope. I would feel the room shaking around 4:30 in the morning and wake up to find Vidal was exercising.

Between my guilt over being away from the children, and the sheer exhaustion that comes with traveling, I would be in need of rehabilitation when I got home. I would drag myself to the gym and try to put myself back together. In the health food store one day, I saw some beautiful women wearing leotards and jeans; they seemed to glow with health. I asked them where they had been and they said they had been to the Yoga College of America. I marched myself down and met Bikhram Choudry, a yoga master from India. He was an attractive man, full of personality. After my kids went off to school, I went to the yoga college for ninety minutes every day. I became very strong and supple.

Yoga is not only work, but a form of meditation. One becomes so concerned with various postures that it is necessary to concentrate on each part of the body, just like playing tennis. With my own body I found that I am much more flexible than I am strong.

Yoga also does incredible things for the skin. Because in yoga the lungs are worked like bellows with deep inhalation and exhalation, the blood rushes to the skin. My chest and arms were pink. My skin was in great condition. I could go all day without any makeup. My eyes were shining and I felt terrific. I began to do more advanced postures.

When I was doing yoga every day, I never had an ache or a pain. On the book tour, I couldn't get to class. My body went into a form of withdrawal. I would have a little kink here, a little low back pain. I realized that yoga wasn't the be-all and end-all, but at the time it worked for me. It was hard work, but it was slow and controlled, which is the way I like to exercise. Ultimately, I started to do brief yoga routines on television shows around the country. I can't believe how much time I spent with my nose buried in the carpets of different television studios.

Vidal and I were asked to be part of a one-hour show to run each week night for thirteen weeks on a local television station in Los Angeles. A different couple would act as host and hostess each night; our night was Wednesday.

We got together, and it was the Sassoon Production Company with offices on the living room floor of our house. Together, we all researched the guests. I did the typing and wrote out the cue cards. We all made suggestions. I worked out an arrangement with Giorgio's, a fabulous boutique on Rodeo Drive, to lend me clothes in return for a credit on the show. We were all putting a lot of time and energy into the show, and I think it was fun to watch. After thirteen weeks, Vidal and I were asked to continue on a half-hour basis each night.

Though it was fun doing the show, it did make me realize that Vidal and I were having problems. Our writers had me doing my little jokes at Vidal. It got easier and easier. I had to hold myself in check so I wouldn't seem hostile. When we were dealing with the guests, Vidal would start the questioning and then he would turn the guest over to me. He didn't need to be in total control for his ego. I was watching and learning all the time.

Vidal had a tendency to get so involved with a guest that he would forget we had only a half hour. He also mixed up names all the time. Instead of Dudley Moore and Peter Cook it would be Dudley Cook and Peter Moore. Things were starting to be a little strained between us and a little feeling of competition was growing between us. There were times when I realized I had taken over, and I had to pull back. He would take over and I would resent it. People would comment favorably or unfavorably depending on whom they identified with. It was upsetting, but there it was.

I was doing the television show, going to school in the mornings, running the house, caring for children, handling my part of our mutual social obligations, and making quick trips for the business. We were decorating the house, and it was my responsibility to deal with the carpenters, plumbers, electricians, and a million other details. I was developing the ability to get things organized and I was feeling very good about myself.

With the book and the television show, my anonymity was really over. At school, people talked to me as Beverly Sassoon and not just another student. People expected more of me, and there was nothing I could do about it. I had also developed a physical weakness. Whenever I would start to feel too much stress, I would come down with pneumonia.

All of this time, we had been having interviews with people from the adoption agency. In all fairness to the child, to our natural children and to us, I knew we couldn't take a child who had either severe physical or emotional problems. The case workers would be at the house interviewing the kids, interviewing us. It was like therapy. They wanted to be sure they were doing the right thing. The child had to be one who could deal with two parents who worked, parents who were part of the public domain. They had to consider whether it would put a strain on a child who might not be altogether attractive to be in an environment committed to health and beauty. There was the racial reality. How did we all really feel about a racially mixed child? What about the reaction of our parents to such a child? How did the other children feel about it?

We had done seventy-eight segments by the time the television show finally ended just before Christmas, and Vidal and I decided to take the children to Aspen. Just before we were to leave, the people from the adoption agency called to say they had a little boy in mind for us. They came over with pictures of cute, two-year-old David. They told us a little bit about him. His mother was white and so was her husband. His mother had three other white children. His own father was unknown. He had been born in Memphis. He had no physical handicap. His emotional handicap was that he had been given up.

It was the greatest Christmas present we could have been given. As soon as we were back in town, Vidal and I drove out to the San Fernando Valley to the foster home where David was staying. The foster parents had already had twenty-three foster children, two of whom they had adopted. The screen door opened and this little person ran across the lawn. He jumped into Vidal's arms and said, "Are you my new daddy?"

Now, here were two adults who had been around a bit. I started to cry. Here was this darling, roly-poly little boy with hardly any hair. (Loss of hair can be caused by anxiety.) There was no turning back. When we were in the house, he came to sit on my lap. "I won't be rough with you," he said. "You're supposed to be nice to ladies."

We wanted him immediately, but the adoption agency people wanted to test it out so he could get used to us and we could get used to him. He would come for a weekend, or a couple of days here and there. Our children loved him. They dragged him all around the neighborhood, introducing him as their new brother. When it was time for him to go back to the foster home, he would cry and so would they. David lived with us for a whole year before we could legally adopt him. It was a hellish year.

I would throw the dirty clothes into the washing machine and turn it on without realizing that David had filled the soap dispenser with bread crusts. He would throw things down the toilet and when I would get home there would be a plumber's truck in the driveway. Once when he was very upset, he set our bed on fire. The fire department had to be called. We were determined to work things out, but I needed every bit of child psychology I was learning, and then some. Still, it was a good feeling. Here was somebody we could give opportunities. We didn't owe David aything in the way we owed our own children, at least not until we adopted him.

My parents didn't say a whole lot about the adoption, but they did make a genuine effort. Whenever Vidal's mother came, she would always bring something for David as well as the others. From time to time, Mrs. Sassoon would take one or another of the children for the weekend. I never asked her to take David.

I added Afro-American history courses to my studies so that when the time came I would be able to pass it along to David. I didn't want to separate him from his background.

I was becoming more and more serious about school and that changed the quality of the time Vidal and I had together. When I first started college, the attitude people seemed to have was, "Oh, isn't that nice? She's found something to amuse herself." In those first days, perhaps, that was my attitude, too, but now I was a disciplined student.

If I had an exam or a paper due, I wouldn't go to a dinner

party the night before, so Vidal would go alone. He thought it was all right for me to go to school, but he couldn't understand why I was knocking myself out.

I wasn't on anybody's coattails at school. Whatever my successes, or failures, the responsibility was all mine. My life at school had nothing to do with the fact that I was married to somebody who was a success. I had been wife and mother and part-time business partner. Now I was somebody who had done a book, co-hosted a television show. I was in college, I tended to our four children, handled our social life, and managed a complicated household.

I enrolled in a criminal law class and picked as my project an evaluation of drug abuse centers. This took me to meetings of Narcotics Anonymous, to Cry Help, a live-in rehabilitation program, Impact House, and to IADARP, a federally funded program for rehabilitation. I spent Christmas Eve day of 1976 in the detoxification ward of the West Valley Community Hospital watching people as they were brought in. It was tough for me to get comfortable. A lot of the people had just gotten out of jail. They still wore the shoes they had been issued.

My involvement with these groups created another strain between Vidal and me. I could put on a scarf and dark glasses and be anonymous. I would never ask him to come along because he would have been too conspicuous. And when I was at home, I would be typing away, organizing my notes.

I completed my two years as an undergraduate on the Dean's Honor List at Santa Monica City College and I was enrolled at UCLA to do my upper division work. Then one day the phone rang. George Shaw, a vice-president of the company, asked me if I would like to do a speaking tour for Cosmetics Week in Australia. UCLA works on the quarter system. If I were away for the two weeks the tour was going to take, it would be crucial. I decided to put off starting UCLA to do the tour. The thought of being on my own in a strange country was irresistible.

❧ 10 ❧

Playing Off-Broadway Down Under

The trip to Australia was the first time I was really on my own. I did two speaking engagements a day over a period of ten days at a chain of department stores in Melbourne and Sydney. I talked to the women who came to hear what I had to say about how to take a good, long, realistic look at themselves and to take a personal inventory of where they were in terms of posture, body shape, hair, skin, hands and feet, where they would like to be, and how to set a fast, easy, fun program to attain their goals. I discussed in detail hair care and diet, exercise and skin care. I talked about how to economize in terms of time by, for example, doing some simple, beneficial stretching exercises at the same time they were moisturizing after a shower. It was only after I got off the stage that the Australian women would crowd around me, and the questions would pour out.

On the plane home, I evaluated what I had learned from the trip. One of the nicest things about being so far away from home was that the tour was really off-Broadway, a place to try out. I had been nervous in the beginning, but what was most evident was that the tour was just a stepped-up version of real life. I had to look great. I had to understand my own physical limitations in order to preserve the energy and stamina I had to have to do the best job I could. For example, I found that if I ate before I made an appear-

75

ance, I would feel lethargic. Instead of eating a meal, I would whip up a high energy protein drink in a borrowed blender.

Australia was a revelation for me. I had tested myself, stretched myself, and I had succeeded—on my own. I had satisfied myself and my audiences that I had evolved into a professional in the health and beauty field. The chapters that follow are a compendium of everything a woman needs to establish a total program of health and beauty care—a program that will give you beauty—for always.

II

My Total
Beauty Program

1

Taking Your Own
Personal Inventory

To know what you have to work with, the first thing to do is to
stand in front of a full-length mirror and take a good, long look at
yourself. At my lectures, when I ask women what they do then,
some say, ''I burst into tears.'' Others say, ''I shut my eyes.''

I've looked into the mirror and I've wanted to burst into tears,
too. I've looked into the mirror and not only have I shut my eyes,
but I've cringed. When I did my own personal inventory after my
daughter, Eden, was born, I saw what gaining forty pounds during
pregnancy can do to you. My muscle tone was awful and I was
fat—fat. I still had twenty-five pounds to lose, and it took me six
weeks. I had to exercise daily and live on fruits and vegetables, but
it had to be done. That was what it took to get my body back in
shape so that I could feel good about myself again.

When I took a personal inventory a month or so after Vidal
and I had gone to court to get our divorce, I saw the toll that the
time of indecision and unhappiness had taken. For months, I had
been ignoring the fact that it was getting a little bit harder each day
to zip up my jeans. I was tired all the time. When I took off my
clothes and looked in the mirror, I saw that I was at least ten
pounds overweight. I hadn't exercised in months and my muscle
tone showed it.

I took myself in hand and started to watch my diet. I did my

79

exercises regularly, starting off with warm-up and stretches, doing each exercise five times and working up, finally, to twenty. At the end of the month I was at my ideal weight, and my fatigue was gone. Once I took that crucial first step of evaluating where I was, I was able to determine what it would take to get from there to where I wanted to be.

There is a difference between looking at yourself realistically and looking at yourself too critically. If you're five feet tall, for example, there's no point to looking in the mirror and thinking that you are ever going to be as tall as Susan Anton. What a personal inventory should cover is posture, hair, skin, body shape and its tone, hands and feet. Some people like to use an accurate bathroom scale and a tape measure to watch the ounces and then the pounds as they melt away. I think we can leave an evaluation to the eye, to the way we look to ourselves, and to the way we feel.

POSTURE

You are wearing the most beautiful Halston gown in the world. Way Bandy or Pablo Manzoni has done your makeup. Your hair is perfect, and you're dripping with the private stock of Harry Winston. If you aren't standing up straight, you're still going to look like a drudge.

Posture makes the first statement of the way we feel about ourselves. If your head is hanging and your shoulders sag, the statement you make is that you don't feel all that good about yourself. Posture is also one area in which we can see an immediate improvement.

Looking into the mirror, throw back your shoulders, raise your chin and tuck in your stomach. In just one second, you can radiate energy and look more confident. Walk like a queen. Good posture says you like yourself. Posture is the first step toward making the most of what you have.

NUTRITION

We must realize that the fuel we put into this wonderful machine that is our body is the most important element of all. We've all heard the old phrase, "You are what you eat." Well, it's true. We wouldn't expect a car to run at its peak performance on the wrong kind of gas, and we can't expect that we will run at our peak performance on the wrong kind of fuel, either. I'm not advocating that you never give in to that impulse for a hot fudge sundae or a baked potato dripping with butter and sour cream. What I am saying is that indulgences like these must be compensated for with sensible eating the next day.

No matter how much you have abused your body with the empty calories found in junk foods, no matter how you have allowed your weight to creep up, your body will forgive you if you remedy these problems. In the chapter, "Nutrition, Health and Weight Control" (p. 101), I have detailed the proper balance of protein, carbohydrates, fat, vitamins, minerals and water that will bring you to the weight you desire, and keep it there.

BODY SHAPE

Even when you have attained the weight you desire, it isn't realistic to think that you will be able to bounce onto a beach in a string bikini. Good muscle tone is just as important as proper body weight. If your inner arms sag, your inner thighs seem to have a limp life of their own, your stomach is oozing over your jeans and your buttocks have the consistency of cottage cheese, it's going to take time and work to restore muscle tone. It's a fact of life that as the years pass, gravity takes over and we lose the marvelous elasticity of youth. In time, every part of our body seems to be reaching for the ground. It is the only by battling this natural tendency that we can be in the shape we want to be and make the very most of what we have.

An inventory of your body shape will reveal its own problem areas, but, once again, be realistic. Nothing is going to change you from a short endomorph with large breasts, hips and thighs to a tall, skinny ectomorph right out of the pages of *Harper's Bazaar*. But problem areas can be minimized. They can look as good and be as firm as possible.

The problem areas with most body shapes are somewhere between the bustline and the knees, although upper arms become flabby early and are difficult, but not impossible, to tone up. Let's look at our rib cage, our waist, our tummy, the outer and inner thighs, which are the first to go, and the hardest to deal with. An aunt of mine used to talk about "fanny fallout." If, when you get out bed, you find yourself fighting the impulse to back out of the room so your husband or lover won't see the state of your rear, you've probably got fanny fallout. Never fear, it can be corrected. Following the warm ups, stretches and spot exercises detailed in the chapter, "What Exercise Is All About" (p. 117), will eventually give you a body shape that is as firm and supple as it can be, and keep it there.

HAIR

When you look at your hair, be realistic. If you have super-fine hair, nothing you can do is going to give you Farrah Fawcett's mane. If it is kinky, the price you'll pay in terms of injury to your hair to straighten it is too high. Instead, get the best possible haircut using the techniques I've outlined to find the right hairdresser for you. And, after a long, hot summer or an icy winter when you are also in and out of overheated houses, offices and stores, your hair may be dry and lifeless. A proper hair care regime, which I've detailed in the chapter, "What Your Hair Is All About" (p. 135), will get your hair back into peak condition and keep it there.

SKIN

If your skin is oily and your pores large, nothing is going to give you the porcelain loveliness of the young Greta Garbo. If your skin is dry and flaky, it's going to take work to bring it into balance. What is necessary is to develop skin awareness. Skin reflects our moods, the state of our health. Proper skin care can make a big difference in the way our skin looks. Proper care of the skin, as detailed in the chapter, "What Your Skin Is All About" (p.149), will return your complexion to a clean, clear, blemish-free state, and keep it there, even after continued abuse by the summer sun or the icy blasts of winter.

CONSIDERING PLASTIC SURGERY

No matter how closely we adhere to the health and beauty program we've developed by trial and error to fit more comfortably into our lives, the day will inevitably come when our skin begins to lose its natural elasticity. With aging, the elastin and collagen that form the connective tissues of our skin are not what they were. We begin to notice a little droop of the eyelids, a tiny droop under the chin and wrinkles that won't go away no matter what we do.

At some point in my lectures, I usually mention that my nose is my own, my teeth are my own, and that I've never had a face lift. I am lucky to have healthy teeth and a nose that satisfies me. But what about the day when I start to notice that droop here, that droop there? Will I think about plastic surgery? You bet I will. I think plastic surgery is an option every older woman has.

If and when that time ever comes, I will know what plastic surgery can and cannot do. It cannot perform miracles. No matter how magical a surgeon's hands, I will never look eighteen again. What plastic surgery can do is make me look better. It will make me look the very best I can look. For any older woman, considering plastic surgery should be part of her personal inventory. Consult the chapter, "What Plastic Surgery Is All About" (p. 169), to see if you might want to consider it.

HANDS AND FEET

If your nails are brittle and splitting, and your cuticles jagged, Cartier's isn't going to kill to have you model its rings after one good manicure. If you have disfigured your feet with badly fitting shoes, you won't be dancing the night away in delicate sandals after your first pedicure, either. Still, as you will learn in the chapter, "Your Hands and Feet" (p. 175), problems with hands and feet can be remedied. They can be the very best they can be.

As you follow the fast, easy, fun plan of action I've detailed in this book to become the best you can be, you will see the glow of health on your fresh, clear, blemish-free skin. You will feel your endurance increase and fatigue vanish as you exercise in a pragmatic, pleasurable way. You will feel your clothes become looser as you gradually and carefully drop those unwanted pounds. You will feel yourself changing for the better. Listen to what your body is telling you. It will be saying that you're on your way to becoming the very most you can be.

2

A Seven-Day Program
of Psychic Push-ups
to Get You in the Frame of Mind
to Start to Be the Very Best You Can Be

Now that you have taken your personal inventory and hit upon a
plan of action, the chances are that you're feeling so overwhelmed
by what lies ahead that all you want to do is forget the whole thing.

There is no reason that I can see to start on your plan of action
all at once. There are little things you can do that will do wonders
for your self-esteem before you actually begin. Because they take
no effort, I call them "Psychic Push-ups." And, remember, there is
no reason for you to be in this all alone. If you have a husband or
lover or children, include them when it is appropriate in your program toward a better you. After all, it's never too early to learn
about proper skin and hair care, establishing a program of diet and
exercise that will make them the very best they can possibly be,
too.

This seven-day program of psychic push-ups starts the night
before. On Saturday, cut out a photograph of someone you think is
fabulous looking, and tape it to the refrigerator. Also, buy a baby

plant. As you watch its development from day to day, it will make you more aware of your own development as you start on a program to become the very best you can be.

Be sure to get a good night's sleep.

SUNDAY—DAY ONE

Before you get up, do the bed stretching described in the chapter on "The Fast, Easy, Fun Morning Routine That Works for Me" (p. 9).

Because you have had a good night's sleep, the face you will see in the bathroom mirror is bright-eyed and awake. Looking into the mirror, review what you did for yourself the day before. Here's how it should go:

"Mary, yesterday you bought a plant you can watch change as you change. You picked out a psychic roommate as an example for you, and you taped her to the refrigerator. You got a good night's sleep so you are bright-eyed and awake."

When you go into the kitchen, take a good look at your psychic roommate before you open the refrigerator. Possibly the sight of her will make your choice of what to have for breakfast a poached egg on dry toast instead of three jelly doughnuts, or a Polish sausage and an English muffin slathered with peanut butter. It doesn't matter. We are not yet starting our disciplined program of becoming the very best we can be. We are only beginning to prepare for it psychologically.

Check your plant.

Get a good night's sleep.

MONDAY—DAY TWO

Do your bed stretching.

Looking into the mirror, recite aloud the list of what you did for yourself the day before. Here's how it should go:

"Mary, yesterday you did your bed stretching in the morning. When you went to the refrigerator, the sight of your psychic roommate did (or didn't) stop you from eating like your next job is the fat lady in the circus. You checked your plant. You got a good night's sleep so you are bright-eyed and wide awake."

While you are still looking into the bathroom mirror, force yourself to list out loud what you like and don't like about your face.

Check your plant.

While you are getting dressed, figure out a time during the day when you can visit a department store to talk to the various cosmetics line representatives about the proper cleansing cream, soap, toner and moisturizer that will work the best to give you a clean, clear, blemish-free skin. You don't have to buy anything; just make yourself aware of the products that are available.

When you walk to the car, bus or subway, walk just a little bit more briskly than you usually would. Walking uses up 216 calories an hour. Walking more briskly than usual uses up more calories than usual. Be aware of your breathing. Consciously try to get that nice, clean fresh air into your lungs. Feel your face getting flushed as your circulation improves.

Start to look around you to try to spot haircuts that would work for you.

Visit the department store and ask about skin care products. Glance at the hair care products and the makeup.

Make a luncheon date for tomorrow with a thin friend.

Get a good night's sleep.

TUESDAY—DAY THREE

Do your bed stretching.

Looking into the mirror, recite aloud the list of what you did for yourself the day before. Here's how it should go:

"Mary, yesterday you did your bed stretching, you checked your plant, and you forced yourself to list out loud what you do like and don't like about your face.

"You walked just a little bit more briskly than you usually do. You thought about your breathing, and how nice it was to get that nice, clean fresh air into your lungs. You felt your face getting flushed as your circulation improved. You looked around to try to spot a haircut that will work for you. You found out about skin care products, and you are now at least vaguely aware of what hair care products and makeup are available. You made an appointment for lunch with Sharri, your thin friend."

While you are making your coffee or tea, elevate onto the balls of your feet, which works your ankles, calves and buttocks. Tuck in your pelvis.

Check your plant.

Walk briskly and be conscious of your breathing.

While at lunch with your thin friend, be aware of the difference in what she eats and what you eat. Look around the restaurant for a haircut that might work for you. On the way back from lunch, stop in and buy cleansing cream, soap, toner, moisturizer, eye cream and body lotion.

Before you go to bed, admire your psychic roommate.

Using the method I've described in the chapter, "The Fast, Easy, Fun Morning Routine That Works for Me," properly cleanse, tone and moisturize your face (p. 9).

Get a good night's sleep.

WEDNESDAY—DAY FOUR

Do your bed stretching.

Properly cleanse, tone and moisturize your face. This is the morning for shower awareness. As you shower, be aware of the lumps and bumps, the tone of your upper arms, your inner and outer thighs, the hints of cellulite, the dry patches of skin. When you get out of the shower, use your body lotion to moisturize toes, heels, calves, thighs, elbows and upper arms.

Looking into the mirror, recite aloud the list of what you did for yourself the day before. Here's how it should go:

"Mary, yesterday you did your bed stretching in the morning. You checked your plant.

"You walked briskly and watched your breathing. You worked your ankles, calves and buttocks with your pelvis tucked in by elevating onto the balls of your feet as you made your morning coffee. While at lunch with your thin friend, you saw the salad she ate and the gooey hamburger you ate, and, even though you did it, you really knew it would be better if you didn't. You also worked the room to find a haircut. You bought what you needed to properly care for your face. You bought body lotion. You washed, toned and moisturized your face and you got a good night's sleep."

While you are making your coffee or tea, elevate. Repeat several times.

Check your plant.

Walk briskly and be conscious of your breathing.

Get the name of a really good hairdresser and make an appointment.

Spend your lunch hour going to the drugstore to buy a Loofah, which is described in the section on the Sensual Shower (p. 11).

On the way back, stop at a health food store and have something for lunch from the light menu you'll find there. Explore the products and pick up some Vitamin E oil, which you'll soon use in a bath.

Instead of what you usually snack on in the early evening, make some popcorn (without butter or salt), put your feet up and watch television. Popcorn is the most emotionally satisfying snack there is. Because we all associate it with Saturday afternoons at the movies, it seems to be deliciously wicked, which is not a bad psychological bonus for only 54 calories a cup.

Have a look at your psychic roommate.

Properly cleanse, tone and moisturize your face.

Get a good night's sleep.

THURSDAY—DAY FIVE

Do your bed stretching.

Properly cleanse, tone and moisturize your face. Take a good look in the mirror. Doesn't your skin look just a little bit better, even in this short a time?

Use the Loofah in the shower as outlined in the section on the Sensual Shower in the chapter on my morning routine and think about the wonderful, tingling way it makes your skin feel. Once out of the shower and barely dry, put your leg up on the counter or the toilet seat and moisturize as your work your ankles, calves and thighs in the bonus stretch described in the chapter on my morning routine.

Looking into the mirror, recite aloud what you did for yourself the day before. Here's how it should go:

"Mary, yesterday you did your bed stretching and your elevations while you made your morning coffee. You properly cared for your skin both morning and evening. While you took your shower, you faced the facts about the tone of your upper arms, your inner and outer thighs and those disgusting hints of cellulite, not to mention the dry patches of skin here and here. You moisturized when you got out of the shower. You checked your plant and your psychic roommate.

"You walked briskly, made an appointment for today with a really good hairdresser, and, instead of eating a big plate of pasta for lunch, you nibbled on lettuce at a health food store and felt none the worse for it. You bought your Vitamin E oil and your Loofah. At the end of the day, instead of falling ravenously on a peanut butter and jelly sandwich to get you through until dinner, you had popcorn, which not only filled you up and made you feel deliciously wicked, but cost you only 54 calories. Mary, I'm beginning to think you're going to pull yourself together.''

While you are making your coffee or tea, elevate. Repeat several times.

Check your plant.

Walk briskly and be conscious of your breathing. When you go to your hairdresser, walk briskly a block past the shop and then walk back. Take along cheese, yogurt and fruit to eat while you are there. Before your hair is washed, be sure your hairdresser sees you the way you want to be seen so he or she will be able to conclude from the way you are dressed, your height and the relationship of your body to your head the way you wish to look and how your haircut should be balanced to show off the rest of you to best advantage. Ask your hairdresser what shampoo, finishing rinse or whatever you should buy in order to take care of your hair at home. Discuss with him or her the possibility of a henna rinse the next time you need a haircut.

When you leave the hairdresser, buy the shampoo and finishing rinse that will work for you. As you shop, start to think about the foods that have always been your downfall, the pastas, breads and desserts you love so much.

That afternoon, try to take a walk in a peaceful environment, like a park. Assuming everything isn't covered with snow, be aware of the colors of the trees and the flowers. Allow the colors to influence you in terms of the new clothes you're going to buy, a possible color for an eyeshadow or a lipstick. Allow the colors to influence you in terms of what you're going to buy the next time you're at the market. The yellows of the trees as they turn might make you think of squashes, melons and apricots. The greens should bring to mind the leafy green vegetables so high in protein and iron.

If you're hungry when you get home, make a cup of popcorn.

Change your psychic roommate.

Properly cleanse your face. Admire your new haircut.

Get a good night's sleep.

FRIDAY—DAY SIX

Do your bed stretching.

Properly cleanse, tone and moisturize your face, while you admire your new haircut. Use your Loofah in the shower, and stretch while you moisturize as you did yesterday.

Looking into the mirror, recite aloud what you did for yourself the day before. Here's how it should go:

''Mary, yesterday you did your bed stretching and your elevations while you made your morning coffee. You properly cared for your skin both morning and evening. You got your circulation going with your Loofah, and you stretched while you applied your moisturizer. You checked your plant, which is flourishing.

''You got a really good haircut, and bought the products you will need to maintain it easily at home. Not only did you walk briskly past the shop and then back to it, but while you were there you lunched on cheese, yogurt and fruits instead of that slop you're usually shoveling into yourself. You really thought about the foods that are your downfall.

''When you took your walk, you were aware of the colors of the flowers and the trees, and you thought of the proper foods that come in the same colors.

''When you got home, you thought about a peanut butter and jelly sandwich and you didn't have it. You thought about popcorn, and you didn't even have that. Instead, you soaked your fingers in olive oil to start to soften your cuticles. Kiddo, I think you're coming along.''

Looking into the bathroom mirror, stretch your arms toward the ceiling. Alternate climbing rope with each arm. Let your arms fall outward, and bend slowly toward the floor.

Increase the number of elevations you do while you are making your morning coffee or tea.

Check your plant.

Walk briskly as usual wherever you go.

Consciously avoid the foods you find dangerous.

Take some time during the day to buy the items you are going to need to give yourself a manicure and a pedicure, which are listed in the chapter on ''Your Hands and Feet'' (p. 175).

Remember your popcorn substitution if you feel hungry when you get home.

Evaluate your lingerie and think about how nice it's going to be when you can do justice to the fragile, feminine little numbers you are going to buy as soon as you are slim and firm.

Admire your psychic roommate.

Properly cleanse, tone and moisturize your face.

Get a good night's sleep.

SATURDAY—DAY SEVEN

Do your bed stretching.

Properly cleanse, tone and moisturize your face, while you admire your new haircut. Use your Loofah in the shower, and stretch while you moisturize. Do the full body stretch and climb rope as you did yesterday.

Looking into the mirror, recite aloud what you did for yourself the day before. Here's how it should go:

"Mary, yesterday you did your bed stretching and your elevations while you made your morning coffee. You properly cared for your skin both morning and evening. You got your circulation going with your Loofah. You stretched while you applied your moisturizer and you did a full stretch and climbed rope. You checked your plant, which is healthy as it can be, and you admired your psychic roommate, and you know you can soon look that good yourself.

"You walked briskly, you ate only what you know is good for you, and you bought everything you need for a manicure and pedicure. You ate some popcorn before you evaluated your lingerie, and you got a good night's sleep. Mary, you are definitely rising in my estimation. You are a woman of willpower and discipline."

Plan an activity for the day that is visually and physically pleasing. Go on a picnic or a bicycle ride with your family or friends. Take along fruits, cheeses and yogurt for your picnic lunch.

Sometime during the day, give yourself the manicure and pedicure detailed in the chapter, "Your Hands and Feet" (p.175).

Before you go out with your husband, lover or friends that evening, take a long, lukewarm bath, using either Vitamin E oil, a couple of tablespoons of olive or safflower oil, or bath salts. As you moisturize and stretch, check your hair. It's cut properly, and if it isn't as shiny and bouncy as it should be, the time will soon come. Look at your skin. After this short a time, doesn't it look better already?

Just by avoiding dangerous foods for a few days, you already seem to be losing pounds even if you aren't, and by walking briskly, your endurance certainly does seem to be increasing. You've given yourself a manicure and a pedicure, and you had that terrific, relaxing bath, which left your skin feeling smooth and sleek. Your plant is just fine, and as for your psychic roommate, she has nothing on you.

When you get home, properly cleanse, tone and moisturize your skin.

These past seven days of psychic push-ups will have proved that you are the disciplined person you know you are. In only one month of following the exercise and diet programs in this book, you will start to notice a body shape closer to your goal, and muscle tone that has already improved. You will be on your way to becoming the very best you can be.

• 3 •

The Rehabilitation Diet

After I took my own personal inventory and realized that it was going to take drastic measures to restore my weight and body shape to what they had been, I decided to consult with a nutritional expert who could outline a program which would give me the fuel for my body that I need while at the same time mobilizing unwanted calories in a slow, controlled way to prevent the unwanted side effect of sagging skin.

A friend suggested I consult with Frank Mosler, M.D., a doctor who specializes in weight control through his Nutrition & Metabology Medical Group in Van Nuys. The following diet, which Dr. Mosler has devised, is a program of approximately 500 calories a day that fuels the body with the protein, carbohydrates, fats, vitamins, minerals and water it needs each day. If you follow this program carefully for three weeks, you can lose ten pounds. Before you begin any weight loss program, it is wise to consult with your own doctor. But this is the program that, together with exercise and relaxation, had me back in the shape I wanted to be in one month.

For a few days before I started Dr. Mosler's Rehabilitation Diet, I forced myself to get eight hours sleep each night. I made a conscious effort to slow down. Whenever I could, I put my feet up. I concentrated on taking deep breaths to force good, clean air into my lungs. Gradually, I began to follow, in order, the warm-ups, stretches and spot exercises which are explained in detail in the

95

chapter, "The Fast, Easy, Fun Way to a Body Shape That Is As Good As It Can Be" (p. 119).

At that point, I began to follow Dr. Mosler's Rehabilitation Diet, which you can find below.

DR. MOSLER'S REHABILITATION DIET

You can eat two meals a day. You can eat them at any time of the day, but you may not eat foods from both meals at the same time. You can break down each meal and eat the fruit or bread between meals instead of with them.

If you want to eat less than the foods allowed in the two meals, you may do so. You may skip part of the entire second meal without upsetting the balance of the body. You are permitted 9 ounces of protein a day. You can either eat 4¹/₂ ounces of protein with each meal, or break them down and eat 3 ounces of protein with each meal, and 3 ounces in the afternoon if you experience a mid-afternoon slump. If you are going to skip any foods, skip foods from the vegetable group, the bread group or the fruit group. Don't skip foods from the protein group.

Each meal consists of one item each from the protein group, the vegetable group, the bread group and the fruit group.

Choose one food from each of the four groups for Meal #1.

Choose one food from each of the four groups for Meal #2.

Group One—155 Grams Protein Food

You have the choice of one of the following items weighing 155 grams (4¹/₂ ounces). This is the raw weight before cooking.

You must weigh the food on a postal or diet scale. The usual household scale is not accurate enough.

The meats you can choose from include:

Chicken Breast
This refers to the white meat (no skin) from the breast of a young fryer chicken.

Chicken Livers
This refers to chicken livers purchased raw and then cooked.

Veal
The following lean cuts only: sirloin, standing rump roast, loin chop.

Lean Beef Hearts
One way to eat this would be to have it ground up and made into patties, seasoned with horseradish. You may prefer to eat it as it comes.

Dried Chipped Beef
(One 3$^1/_2$-ounce package is equivalent to a 100-gram serving.) With this item, there may be no weight loss for a few days because of the salt content and subsequent water retention. However, a loss of fat will still occur, and the water will be lost eventually. This item is included mainly for convenience, because no other beef is allowed.

The seafoods you can choose from are:

White Fish
Fresh frozen or unbreaded sole, flounder, haddock, pollack, perch, pike, white sea bass, halibut, turbot, water-packed tuna and salmon.

Shellfish
Lobster, crab and shrimp. These are desirable because they are very lean. It is recommended that you use them often.

Miscellaneous
The whites only of 6 hard-boiled eggs. Like the water-packed tuna or salmon, this is good for a quick meal. We don't recommend, however, that you eat egg whites twice a day every day.

Hoop Cheese
This is the same as farmer or pot cheese. It is an excellent item, but you have to learn how to prepare it. We suggest you start out by mixing it with water and Lawry's seasoning to make it the consistency of cottage cheese. It is the only cheese allowed.

Group Two—Vegetable Group

You may choose one type only from the following list. You may not mix more than one kind at each meal. You may have a normal serving of one kind for each meal. This is about $^1/_2$ to 1 cup, depending on the vegetable used.

Your choices include:

Asparagus	Dill (sour)	Onions
Beet	pickles	Parsley
greens	Endive	Radishes
Cabbage	Escarole	Spinach
Celery	Fennel	String
Chard	Kale	beans
Chicory	Lettuce	Summer
Chinese	Mung bean	squash
cabbage	sprouts	Tomatoes
Cucumbers	Mushrooms	Watercress

Remember that there are no substitutions.

Dressings
No butter or oil may be used to prepare these vegetables. Several commercial dressings, labeled 2 calories per tablespoon, are available to cook your vegetables or to use as dressings on salads. No other dressings may be substituted.

Group Three—Bread Group

You have the choice of one each of the following:

1 average-sized bread stick

Melba toast

Finn Crisp cracker (very thin)

1 square Norwegian flatbread

$1/3$ of an English muffin

Group Four—Fruit Group

You have the choice of one each of the following:

1 apple, orange or a handful of strawberries

$1/2$ cantaloupe or grapefruit

$1/4$ casaba or honeydew melon

$1/2$ papaya

$1/2$ cup sugar-free cooked rhubarb (may be artificially sweetened)

$^1/_2$ cup water-packed and/or artificially sweetened sliced peaches, apricots or gooseberries

1 cup low-calorie gelatin dessert

The following items are also allowed:

The juice of one lemon daily for all purposes.

One tablespoon of milk per day.

Salt, Lawry's seasoning, pepper, vinegar, dry mustard powder, garlic, sweet basil, thyme, or other seasonings, but no oil, butter or regular dressing. There is a new product on the market called Butter Buds which is acceptable as a butter substitute. It has 3 calories per tablespoon. It should be used in moderation.

Any amount of water, black coffee or tea; dietetic colas and sodas marked 2 calories per bottle or less; artificial sweeteners. Anytime.

It is important that eight 8-ounce glasses of water be consumed daily. The easiest way to remember how much water must be consumed is to fill two quart containers or one half-gallon container and put it in the refrigerator at night. This amount must be consumed before bedtime the next night.

4

Nutrition, Health and Weight Control

Nutrition is the relationship of the foods we eat to the health of our bodies. Proper nutrition means we are getting the nutrients we need through the food we eat and vitamin supplements to see to it that our health is the very best it can possibly be. Proper nutrition is essential for normal organ development and functioning, normal cell reproduction, growth and maintenance, for our optimum activity level and working efficiency, for resistance to infection and disease, and for the body's ability to repair damage and injury.

The foods we eat are chemically complex. They are broken down by our bodies into simpler chemical forms so that they can be taken in through the intestinal walls and transported by the blood to the cells. There they provide the energy and the correct building materials to maintain us. These chemical processes are digestion, absorption and metabolism.

DIGESTION

Digestion is a series of physical and chemical changes by which food is broken down in preparation for absorption from the intestinal tract into the bloodstream. These changes take place in the digestive tract, which includes the mouth, pharynx, esophagus, stomach, small intestine and large intestine.

101

The active materials in the digestive juices which bring about the chemical breakdown of food are called enzymes. These complex proteins are capable of inducing chemical changes in other substances without changing themselves. Foodstuffs leave the stomach and enter the small intestine in the following order: carbohydrates, protein and fat (which takes the longest to digest).

ABSORPTION

Absorption is the process by which nutrients in the form of glucose (from carbohydrates), amino acids (from protein) and fatty acids and glycerol (from fats) are taken up by the intestines and passed into the bloodstream to facilitate cell metabolism.

METABOLISM

At this point the handling of food within the body has reached its final stage. The process of metabolism involves all the chemical changes that nutrients undergo from the time they are absorbed until they either become a part of the body or are excreted from the body. Metabolism is the conversion of the digested nutrients into building material for living tissue or the energy to meet the needs of our bodies.

SOURCES OF CALORIES

The primary sources of energy for our bodies are carbohydrates, fats and proteins. Their fuel potential is expressed in calories, a term that expresses the amount of energy that may be released as heat when food is metabolized. Foods high in energy value are high in calories and, conversely, foods low in energy value are low in calories. Fats yield approximately 9 calories per gram. Carbohydrates and proteins yield approximately 4 calories per gram.

Carbohydrates

Carbohydrates are the main source of energy for our bodies and they also assist in the digestion of proteins and fats. The principal carbohydrates present in foods are sugars, starches and cellulose. Simple sugars, such as those in honey and fruits, are very easy to digest. Starch can be found in bread and cereals. Cellulose, found in the skins of fruits and vegetables, is largely indigestible, and it contributes little energy value to the diet, but it is necessary because it provides the bulk for proper intestinal action.

Carbohydrate snacks containing sugar and starch provide the body with almost instant energy because they cause a sudden rise in the blood sugar level. It drops rapidly. If you overindulge in starch and sweet foods you may be crowding out other essential foods, which can result in nutritional deficiency and obesity.

Fats

The most concentrated source of energy in the diet comes from fats. Fats furnish more than twice the number of calories per gram furnished by carbohydrates or proteins. Not only do fats provide energy, they also act as carriers for the fat-soluble Vitamins A, D, E, and K. By aiding in the absorption of Vitamin D, fats help make calcium available to body tissues, particularly to the bones and teeth.

Fatty acids give fats their different flavors. The two types of fatty acids are saturated and unsaturated. Saturated fatty acids are those that are usually hard at room temperature, such as butter and margarine. Unsaturated fatty acids, including polyunsaturates, are usually liquid at room temperature and are derived from vegetable, nut, or seed sources, such as corn, safflowers, sunflowers and olives. Other sources of fat are milk products, eggs and cheese. An intake of fat providing 25 to 30 percent of the calories in your diet daily is compatible with good health.

Protein

Next to water, protein is the most plentiful substance in the body. Protein is one of the most important elements for the maintenance of good health and vitality. It is of primary importance in the growth and development of all of the tissues in our bodies. It is the major source of building materials for muscles, blood, skin, hair, nails and internal organs, including the heart and the brain. Most meats and dairy products are complete protein foods.

NUTRIENTS

A knowledge of nutrients and how they function in our bodies is necessary to understand the importance of good nutrition. The six nutrients—carbohydrates, fats, protein, vitamins, minerals and water—are present in the foods we eat and contain chemical substances that furnish the body with heat and energy, provide material for growth and repair of the body tissues and assist in the regulation of body processes.

Vitamins

There are about twenty substances believed to be active as vitamins in human nutrition. With a few exceptions, the body cannot synthesize vitamins. We must get them from the food we eat or from dietary supplements. While many people in the beauty and health fields swear by dietary supplements, I have never found such supplements to be useful except in special circumstances. No combination I have ever tried has made me feel any better than I do when I stick to a well-balanced diet and get my vitamins from their natural sources. (See the chart on p. 105.)

Vitamins have no caloric or energy value, but as constituents of enzymes, which function as catalysts in nearly all metabolic reactions, they help to regulate metabolism, help to convert fats and carbohydrates into energy and assist in forming bone and tissues.

Minerals

Minerals are nutrients that exist in the body and in all food. Approximately seventeen minerals are essential in human nutrition. Although only four or five percent of the human body is mineral, they are vital to overall mental and physical well-being. Minerals are constituents of the bones, teeth, tissue, muscle, blood and nerve cells. They are important in maintaining physiological processes, strengthening skeletal structures and in preserving the vigor of the heart and brain, the muscle and nervous system.

They act as catalysts for many biological reactions within the body, including muscle response, the transmission through the nervous system, digestion and metabolism or utilization of nutrients in foods. They are important in the production of hormones. Minerals help to maintain the delicate water balance essential to the proper functioning of mental and physical processes.

To aid you in developing the balanced diet you need to give yourself what your body needs, following this section is a chart (p. 105) defining the vitamins and minerals you need, what each of them does for you, and the foods in which they are found.

Vitamins and Minerals
What They Do for You and Where You Find Them

Vitamins	*What They Do for You*	*Where You Find Them*
Vitamin A	Aids in growth and repair of body; maintains smooth, soft skin	Fish liver oil; cream; butter; leafy green vegetables; carrots
Vitamin B Complex	Metabolizes fats and proteins; maintains muscle tone, nerves, skin, hair, eyes, mouth, liver	Brewer's yeast; liver; whole grain cereals; green vegetables
Vitamin C	Maintains collagen and protein necessary for formation of connective tissue in skin, ligaments, bones; heals wounds; forms red cells	Citrus fruits; other fresh fruits; vegetables
Vitamin D	Absorption of calcium	Sunlight; Vitamin D enriched milk
Vitamin E	Cellular respiration of muscles; resilience of cells	Wheat germ; seeds; golden vegetable oils, such as safflower, soy and corn
Vitamin F	Respiration of vital organs; maintains resilience of cells	vegetable oils; seeds; cod liver oil
Vitamin K	Forms chemical required in blood clotting; liver functioning	Kelp; alfalfa; green vegetables; milk; egg yolks; red meat; polyunsaturated oils

Minerals	*What They Do for You*	*Where You Find Them*
Aluminum	No function. Can be dangerous	Meats and vegetables; some baking powders; some white flours
Beryllium	Dangerous	
Cadmium	No function	Refined foods, such as flour, rice, white sugar; coffee and tea
Calcium	Builds and maintains bones and teeth; assists in	Milk and dairy products

Minerals	What They Do for You	Where You Find Them
	blood clotting; muscle growth	
Chlorine	Balances acid and alkali in blood; stimulates liver	Table salt; ripe olives
Fluorine	Increases dispersal calcium to strengthen bones	Fluoridated water; seafoods; gelatin
Iodine	Regulates energy; promotes growth and development; aids condition of hair, nails, skin, teeth	All kinds of fish; mushrooms (if grown in iodine-rich soil)
Iron	Produces hemoglobin to transport oxygen in blood to body tissues	Liver; oysters; heart; lean meats; leafy green vegetables
Lead	highly toxic	
Magnesium	Helps to promote absorption and metabolism of other minerals and vitamins; aids bone growth; aids functioning of nerves and muscles	Green vegetables; wheat germ; soybeans; figs; corn; apples; seeds; nuts, especially almonds
Manganese	Aids in utilization of fatty acids and cholesterol; helps to maintain sex hormone production; nourishes nerves and brain	Whole grain cereals; egg yolks; green vegetables
Mercury	Toxic	Can be ingested by eating fish from polluted waters
Molybdenum	Mobilizes iron from liver reserves; oxidizes fats	Legumes; cereal grains; leafy dark-green vegetables
Nickel	Catalyst in hydrogenation of vegetable oils	Corn, peanut and cottonseed oil.
Phosphorus	Found in every cell of body; plays part in almost every chemical reaction	Meat; fish; poultry; eggs; whole grains; seeds; nuts
Potassium	Regulates water balance; necessary for normal growth; stimulates nerve	All vegetables, especially leafy green vegetables; oranges; whole grains;

Minerals	What They Do for You	Where You Find Them
	impulses; keeps skin healthy	sunflower seeds; potatoes; bananas
Selenium	Works with Vitamin E to promote normal body growth and fertility	Bran and germ of cereals; vegetables, such as broccoli, onions and tomatoes; tuna
Sodium	Functions with potassium to regulate water balance of body	Table salt; seafoods; carrots; beets; poultry; meat
Sulfur	Works with other constituents to aid tissue respiration and build cells; called nature's ''beauty mineral'' because it keeps the hair glossy and smooth, and the skin clear and youthful	Meat; fish; legumes; nuts; eggs; cabbage; dried beans; brussels sprouts
Vanadium	Part of circulatory regulating system	Fish
Zinc	Related to normal absorption and action of vitamins; component of insulin; part of enzyme needed to break down alcohol; essential for general growth and proper development of reproductive organs	Foods high in protein; whole grain products; brewer's yeast; wheat bran; wheat germ; pumpkin seeds

Water

Water is not only the most abundant nutrient found in the body but the most important. It is responsible for and involved in nearly every body process, including digestion, absorption, circulation and excretion. It is the primary transporter of nutrients throughout the body, and it helps to maintain a normal body temperature. It is essential for carrying waste material out of the body. The average adult body contains approximately 45 quarts of water and loses about 3 quarts daily through excretion and perspiration, depending on the rate of activity. It is found in nearly all foods that are absorbed by the body. Fruits and vegetables are especially good sources of chemically pure water. Because water keeps the cells healthy, it is recommended that a conscious effort be made to drink sufficient amounts.

WHAT YOU SHOULD KNOW ABOUT CALORIES

The calorie is a unit of measure. It expresses the heat-producing or energy-producing value of food. The statement that a tablespoon of honey contains about 100 calories means that when oxidized by the body, it will release that amount of energy, which the body can then use. As a rule, there are 4 calories per gram in proteins and carbohydrates, and 9 calories per gram in fats. Some fats, some carbohydrates, some proteins and some natural sugars are essential to the functioning of the body each day. What a proper diet does is get the best balance of what the body must have for the fewest number of calories.

To find out your individual requirements, here's a formula that nutritionists use:

Make a note of the weight at which you know you look and feel your best. Multiply that number by 15 if you are between the ages of 35 and 55. If you are between 18 and 35, add 200. If you are 55 or over, subtract 300.

$$
\begin{array}{lrl}
\text{EXAMPLE:} & \text{Perfect Weight} & 125 \text{ pounds} \\
& & \underline{\times 15} \\
& & 1{,}875 \text{ calories (35–55)} \\
& 1{,}875 + 200 = & 2{,}075 \text{ calories (18–35)} \\
& 1{,}875 - 300 = & 1{,}575 \text{ calories (55 and} \\
& & \text{over)}
\end{array}
$$

The figure at which you have arrived is the number of calories you need to maintain your ideal weight. Use the same procedure with your actual weight. Let's say your actual weight is 135 pounds. Multiplying by 15, you get a figure of 2,025. This means you are currently getting a daily oversupply of 150 calories. Only part of the answer lies in cutting 150 calories a day from your diet. Each pound of extra fat you carry represents a previous oversupply of 3,500 calories. In addition to reducing your present and future intake, you also have to eliminate your caloric stockpile of 35,000 calories. To do this, you must force your body to give them up.

If you will glance again at the simple equation above, you will see that as you grow older, you need fewer calories to maintain your body at its optimum weight. Even with a well-balanced diet of lean meats, fish, poultry, vegetables and fruits, the rule for the older woman to remember is less is more.

Calories are burned constantly, but the body burns them rapidly or slowly depending on what it needs to perform its task.

When you're sleeping, the body needs only 30 calories an hour. Sitting up in bed raises the number of calories your body burns to 1.3 per minute. If you go for a walk, you burn 5.2 calories per minute. If you swim or run for 45 minutes, you use up 500 calories. If you just put a little more effort into what you do in the normal course of your day, you'll be burning up calories you don't want. After all, if you go for a five-mile walk in the country, you will burn up no more calories than if you walk five miles at the office during the course of an entire day.

I've never cared for the word diet. All it really means is what you eat. If you say that you're dieting, it can just as accurately mean you're living on hot fudge sundaes as on lean meats, green vegetables, fruits and good, brown whole grain bread. To reach the goal of the ideal body shape and weight, it's going to take exercise and it's going to mean forcing the body to give up the calories it has stored by eating less in a well-balanced way that still provides the body with what it needs, and using up calories by doing more vigorously what you do anyway.

Accomplishing your goals doesn't have to be all that bad. Following this section, you will find a chart listing twenty foods that will give you the highest amount of protein and cost you the lowest number of calories (p. 110). You will also find a chart of low-calorie foods you can substitute for foods with higher calories (p.111). For example, if a half-inch slice of pound cake is only 140 calories and a piece of frosted chocolate cake is 235 calories, why not eat the pound cake and save 95 calories?

There is also a chart (p. 112) to tell you how many calories you are burning up when you do things during the day. For example, if, as you will see, you use only 132 calories an hour while you are at your desk, you will see the advantage of walking a bit more briskly, which burns up 216 calories an hour.

When it seems to me that my clothes are getting a little tight, I go on what essentially is an easy, 24-hour fast. At noon, I have a giant salad with everything in it. The salad will get me through until bedtime, even if I have to make it an early one. I sleep for my usual eight hours. When morning comes, it seems like no time at all until noon rolls around again, and I've managed to complete a 24-hour cleansing process.

If you intend to try to fast for a day or two at the beginning of your self-care program, I would suggest you drink plenty of water and consider taking nutritional supplements. Any fasting program that continues for more than two days should be done only under a doctor's supervision.

The Twenty Foods With the
Highest Proteins in the Lowest Number of Calories

Amount	Food	Calories	Protein (in Grams)	Calories to Protein
3 oz.	shrimp (canned)	100	21	(or 1 gr. protein in 4.10 cals.)
4 oz.	cottage cheese (uncreamed)	85	17	(or 1 gr. protein in 5 cals.)
3 oz.	crabmeat (canned)	85	15	(or 1 gr. protein in 5.10 cals.)
3 oz.	clams (raw, meat only)	65	11	(or 1 gr. protein in 5.10 cals.)
3 oz.	chicken (skinned and broiled)	115	20	(or 1 gr. protein in 5.15 cals.)
2 oz.	dried chipped beef (uncooked)	115	19	(or 1 gr. protein in 6.02 cals.)
3 oz.	fish (non-oily types, baked)	135	22	(or 1 gr. protein in 6.03 cals.)
2–4 oz.	round steak (lean, broiled)	130	21	(or 1 gr. protein in 6.04 cals.)
2.6 oz.	lamb (lean, chop, broiled)	140	21	(or 1 gr. protein in 6.14 cals.)
3 oz.	turkey (roasted)	93.6	13.4	(or 1 gr. protein in 7 cals.)
3 oz.	salmon (water-packed, canned)	120	17	(or 1 gr. protein in 7.01 cals.)
4 oz.	bean sprouts (from soybeans, raw)	23	3	(or 1 gr. protein in 7.02 cals.)
3 oz.	tuna (water-packed, canned)	170	24	(or 1 gr. protein in 7.16 cals.)
3 oz.	hamburger (lean, broiled)	185	23	(or 1 gr. protein in 7.24 cals.)
4 oz.	oysters (raw)	80	10	(or 1 gr. protein in 8 cals.)
1 T.	brewer's yeast	25	3	(or 1 gr. protein in 8.01 cals.)
1 oz.	Swiss cheese (natural)	105	8	(or 1 gr. protein in 8 cals.)
3 oz.	corned beef (canned)	185	22	(or 1 gr. protein in 8.09 cals.)
2 oz.	liver (beef, fried)	130	15	(or 1 gr. protein in 8.10 cals.)
3 oz.	sardines, drained of oil (canned)	175	20	(or 1 gr. protein in 8.15 cals.)

Substituting Less for More

Traditional Food	Calorie-Saving Food	Calories Saved
Apple pie, ¹/₆ of pie (410)	Baked apple (195)	215
Bagel (165)	Rye toast, 1 slice (60)	105
Beef, lean chuck, 4 oz. (180)	Beef, lean round, 4 oz. (150)	30
Cheese, American, 1 oz. (105)	Cheese, Mozzarella, 1 oz. (80)	25
Chicken, fried, 4 oz. (235)	Chicken, broiled, 4 oz. (150)	85
Chocolate cake, frosted, ¹/₁₆ of cake (235)	Pound cake, ¹/₂-inch slice (140)	95
Chocolate pudding, ¹/₂ cup (190)	Chocolate junket, ¹/₂ cup (120)	70
Clam chowder, New England, 1 cup (150)	Clam chowder, Manhattan, 1 cup (75)	75
Corn muffin (130)	Refrigerator biscuit (80)	50
Cream, light, 1 tablespoon (31)	Half-and-half, 1 tablespoon (20)	10
Cream of chicken soup, 1 cup (170)	Chicken noodle soup, 1 cup (65)	105
Egg, fried (110)	Egg, poached, soft or hard-boiled (80)	30
English muffin (145)	Toast, 2 slices (120)	25
Fruit cocktail, canned, ¹/₂ cup (95)	Fruit salad, unsweetened, ¹/₂ cup (55)	40
Grapefruit juice, sweetened, 1 cup (130)	Grapefruit juice, unsweetened, 1 cup (100)	30
Ice cream, 16 percent butterfat, 1 cup (375)	Ice cream, 10 percent butterfat, 1 cup (280)	95
Ice cream, 1 cup (280)	Ice milk, 1 cup (200)	80
Mayonnaise, 1 tablespoon (100)	Salad dressing, 1 tablespoon (65)	35
Milk, whole, 8 oz. (160)	Milk, skimmed, 8 oz. (90)	70
Orange juice, ¹/₂ cup (55)	Tomato juice, ¹/₂ cup (25)	30
Pecan pie, ¹/₆ of pie (570)	Pumpkin pie, ¹/₆ of pie (320)	250
Pineapple, canned, 1 slice with 2 tablespoons syrup (90)	Pineapple, canned in juice, 1 slice with 2 tablespoons juice (70)	20
Potatoes, fried, homemade, 10 pieces (155)	Potatoes, fried from frozen, 10 pieces (125)	30
Potato chips, 10 (115)	Popcorn, unbuttered, 1 cup (54)	61

Traditional Food	Calorie-Saving Food	Calories Saved
Quinine water, 8 oz. (85)	Club soda, 8 oz. (0)	85
Ricotta cheese, $^1/_2$ cup (170)	Cottage cheese, creamed, $^1/_2$ cup (120)	50
Salad oil for cooking, 1 tablespoon (125)	Butter or margarine for cooking (100)	25
Salmon, canned sockeye, 4 oz. (200)	Salmon, canned pink or chum, 4 oz. (160)	40
Sweet potatoes, candied, $^1/_2$ cup (295)	Winter squash, buttered, $^1/_2$ cup (95)	200
Yogurt, strawberry, 8 oz. (290)	Yogurt, vanilla, 8 oz. (220)	70

Spending Caloric Energy per Hour

Activity	Calories	Activity	Calories
Dancing	330	Lawn mowing	462
Bed making	234	Painting at an easel	120
Bowling	264	Piano playing	150
Bricklaying	240	Preparing a meal	198
Carpentry	408	Scrubbing floors	216
Desk work	132	Sitting and eating	84
Driving	168	Sitting and reading	72
Golf	300	Skiing	594
Racquet ball	612	Sleeping	60
Horseback riding	480	Swimming	300
Ironing	252	Walking	216

If the idea of fasting doesn't appeal to you, you can eat only fruits and vegetables for a couple of days. Eat as much lettuce, cauliflower, tomatoes, cucumbers, zucchini and asparagus as you like. The fruits you can eat are apples, oranges and grapefruit. Fruits such as bananas, and vegetables such as peas and beans should be avoided. They retain fluids and, if you eat them, so will you. For these two days only, and I emphasize *only*, you've eaten all you want, and you've taken in no protein at all. Keep in mind that the body must have protein, and going longer than a couple of days without it can be bad for your health.

Until I reach my ideal weight, I avoid red meat. It's a marvelous source of protein, but it's also a source of fat. Seven ounces of porterhouse steak has 216 calories of protein and 268 calories of fat for a total of 484. Seven ounces of ground chuck has 218 calories of protein and 308 calories of fat for a total of 526. Consider that 7 ounces of roast chicken has 312 calories of protein and only 54 calories of fat for a total of 366, or that a veal cutlet has 226 calories of protein and 78 calories of fat for a total of 304, and you will see why I don't eat red meat on a daily basis. There are hundreds of ways to prepare chicken, which is high in protein and low in fat, without frying it. Turkey and veal are low in calories, and so is fish, which can be prepared in many delicious, nonfattening ways.

When you're trying to lose weight, the ultimate luxury is to go away to a spa for a planned program of rehabilitation where someone else does all the thinking for you—every temptation has been removed from your path! I've gone to the Golden Door many times and have found that almost every guest there follows their famous Virtue-Making Diet for at least one day and then asks for a copy to take home. This diet is a great way to start a new fitness program; it is also the perfect antidote to a long party weekend or a long period of concentrated sedentary work. Because the Virtue-Making Diet provides the body with continuous blood sugar builders, it never makes me feel either hungry or weak. It is *not* advised for those who suffer from diabetes, hypoglycemia, or any condition requiring medical care.

When I follow this plan, I give up my customary cups of tea. Coffee is to be avoided as well. Herb teas, though, are fine, and so is freshly squeezed lemonade, and as much spring water as you like. Before each mini-meal or juice break, step outside no matter what the weather. Inhale and exhale very, very slowly twenty times.

When you eat the meals use a demitasse spoon to consume the liquids. Nibble slowly on the hulled, raw, unsalted sunflower seeds. You'll see why the first guest to follow this regime named it the Virtue-Making Diet. It makes you feel like a saint!

If you've let yourself go to the point where you are ten pounds or more over your ideal weight, the Virtue-Making Diet, my 24-hour fast, or a couple of days of eating only fruits and vegetables will let your body know it is no longer going to have to fight to keep up with the excess food you are consuming. It will be ready to accept smaller, well-balanced portions of proteins, carbohydrates and fats, and you will be on your way to the body size and shape that will be the very best it can be.

The Golden Door's Virtue-Making Diet

8:00 A.M. *Grapefruit Juice*
4 oz. freshly squeezed grapefruit juice
2 oz. water

Mix and serve

10:30 A.M. *Almond Milk*
6 whole almonds, blanched and peeled
$1/2$ medium-sized ripe banana
$1/2$ cup water
2 ice cubes
Few drops fresh lemon juice
Dash of vanilla
Pinch of nutmeg

Place in a blender, liquefy and serve

1:00 P.M. *Gazpacho*
1 medium-sized tomato, peeled and diced
$1/4$ large cucumber, peeled and chopped
$1/4$ large green pepper, seeded and chopped
1 onion slice
2 sprigs parsley

Place in a blender, liquefy and serve

3:30 P.M. *Pineapple–Cucumber Juice*
3 oz. cucumber, peeled
1 oz. fresh pineapple
2 sprigs parsley
2 oz. apple juice

Place in a blender, liquefy and serve

6:00 P.M. *Almond Milk*

8:30 P.M. *Carrot–Apple Juice*
2 oz. carrot juice
2 oz. apple juice
$1/2$ apple, peeled

Place in a blender, liquefy and serve.

NOTE: You may eat $1/2$ ounce sunflower seeds with each mini-meal, except the Almond Milk at 10:30 A.M.

Economical Snacks to Give You the Most Satisfaction for the Fewest Calories

The only diets that work are those that satisfy you while you lose weight. Most weight-losing programs forbid snacks because they conjecture that today's raw carrot is tomorrow's hot fudge sundae. I think you can lose weight and have the snacks you are used to as long as you know you are staying within the calorie limit you have set up for yourself. Here are some of the snacks you probably eat anyway, and some that you haven't thought of.

Snack	Calories
Apple (1 average size)	80
Apricots (3 average size)	55
Banana (1 average size)	85
Brazil nuts (4 or 5)	100
Camembert cheese (1 oz.)	85
Carrot (1 raw)	25
Cashew nuts (7)	75
Cinnamon wafers (4)	80
Grapes (1 cup)	93
Honeydew melon (1/4)	65
Nectarine (1 average size)	30
Orange (1 average size)	60
Oatmeal cookie (1 average size)	60
Peach (1 average size)	35
Popcorn (1 cup plain)	54
Pretzel sticks (15 small)	60
Raisins (1 oz.)	60
Swiss cheese (1 ounce)	95
Tangerine (1 average size)	40
Wheat Thins (5)	50

◆・5・◆

What Exercise Is All About

A healthy body is the result of proper nutrition combined with a regular pattern of physical exercise. Exercise imparts vigor and activity to all organs and secures and maintains the healthful integrity of all their functions. Exercise improves the tone and quality of muscle tissue and stimulates the process of digestion, absorption, metabolism and elimination. It also strengthens the blood vessels, lungs and heart, which results in the improved transfer of oxygen to the cells, and increased circulation of the blood and lymph system. Exercise also develops grace, poise and symmetry of the body and can help to correct defective development or to recover from injuries.

TYPES OF EXERCISE

Calisthenics

Calisthenics consists of light exercises or gymnastics, including sit-ups, push-ups, jumping jacks, etc., which promote grace and health. The emphasis in calisthenics is on building skeletal muscles.

Stretching

Stretching is a natural exercise that should be practiced on a regular basis. A good habit to develop is stretching upon rising in the morning and throughout the day. Stretch exercises tend to increase both energy and endurance for all parts of the body. Stretching tends to relieve many aches and pains, loosens up ligaments, joints and muscles. It increases coordination and suppleness. Stretching stimulates circulation and alleviates the stiffness of contracted muscles.

Dancing

Dancing or rhythmic exercises can be a pleasurable way to exercise the body thoroughly and refresh the mind. Besides toning the muscles, joints, glands, respiratory system and digestive organs, it can give everyday movements grace and poise.

Isometrics

Isometric exercise involves the pressure of a muscle or group of muscles against each other or against an immovable object. It is especially good for reducing because it can be applied to specific areas. Isometrics primarily tone and build the skeletal muscles.

Jogging

Jogging is a form of exercise that consists of alternately walking and running. It is an excellent exercise for improving the heart, lungs and circulatory system by expanding their capacity to handle stress. It can help to build muscle tone, reduce hips and thighs, redistribute weight and flatten the abdomen.

Walking

Walking is one of the best overall exercises. It helps the entire system to function better.

◆► 6 ◄◆

The Fast, Easy, Fun Way to a Body Shape That Is As Good As It Can Be

Most of us find it difficult to stick to a program of regular exercising because it is hard work and an eternity seems to pass before we see the slightest result. I don't believe it has to be that way. Exercise should be a source of pleasure. Our bodies are made to be used. It has to feel good to stretch, to get our circulation going, to feel healthier and firmer.

There are many exercises that work, and it's important to try them out. We must listen to our bodies to see what works best. My whole approach to health and beauty is to attain my goals at the lowest price in terms of time and energy. Over the years, there are few exercise programs I haven't tried. I've tried yoga, isometrics, jogging, calisthenics, dancing, running, walking. You name it and I've tried it. Parts of some of them have worked and parts of some of them haven't. I've taken the parts from each of them that seem to get the best results and incorporated them in a system that doesn't take long to do, that doesn't leave me aching and worn out, and that gives me pleasure as I use my body.

Like everybody else, I'm not perfect. For months, I've done no more than my two minutes of bed stretching before I get up in the morning. But for me, it isn't how much exercise I do, but the quality of what I do. I entertain no ambition to make the U.S. Olympic Wrestling Team. I don't want the overdeveloped muscles of a professional athlete. What I do want is to look the very best I can. I want my body to be as firm and healthy as it can possibly be.

I exercise in front of a full-length mirror, so that I can watch myself to make sure I'm getting the most out of each movement in the most graceful way. I exercise to music, and I exercise slowly. The exercise program I have evolved consists of three parts to be done sequentially: warming-up, stretching and exercises to firm and strengthen each specific part of the body.

Stretching to lengthen my muscles is a part of my daily discipline. It prepares my body for the day, circulating the blood to the tissues and muscles. Doing isolated movements to work on certain problem areas without warming-up and stretching isn't wise. You can hurt yourself. If you're working to firm up your stomach, for example, you can pull out your back if you don't prepare your body first.

I think about my body in thirds. The upper third starts at the top of my head and stops just below my breasts. I work my shoulders and neck to keep them relaxed, and to control the fatty area that can accumulate at the back of my neck. I work my upper arms to control the flab that appears at an unreasonably early time in our lives.

The middle third of my body extends from below my breasts to my knees. This includes the problem areas of stomach, waist, lower back, buttocks, inner thighs, outer thighs and the knees.

The bottom third of my body includes my calves, ankles and feet.

If you want to find out if you need to work on your legs, raise a leg and flex it to find out how much fat and how much muscle you have. If you can pinch more than an inch on the top of your thigh, you have unused muscle which needs to be tightened. Thighs are easy to firm up because the muscles are long and large. Don't be surprised if your legs are sore when you first start my exercise program. It's natural, and the soreness will go away in a few days. Getting results doesn't mean you have to hurt.

The lower abdomen is more difficult to firm up than the upper abdomen. Exercising the lower abdomen can result in a stiff upper back and a sore neck. Concentrate on exercising slowly in the beginning. Hold each position for a moment.

Believe it or not, any problem with the buttocks is curable. There is only one major muscle in the buttocks, and it is inactivity that makes it start to drop. When you are exercising your buttocks, remember to tuck in your pelvis. In the beginning, you're going to be sore. Just visualize somebody's big, fat rear on the escalator in front of you, and you'll welcome the pain as your buttock muscles start to become firm.

Warming-up and stretching are to prepare the body for exercise. Together, warming-up and stretching take between 5 and 7 minutes. While warming-up and stretching should be done each day, the remedial exercises should only be done 3 times a week for optimum results. When I go back to my warming-up, stretching and exercise program, I do each warm-up and stretch as designated. I try to do each exercise 5 times. Over a period of a month, I gradually increase the number of times I do each exercise. My goal is to be able to do each of them 20 times.

WARMING-UP—DAILY ROUTINE

1. Face the mirror. With your feet together, bring your arms over your head and put your palms together. Bend to each side. (See illustration.) Do this twice. Warming-up and stretching are only to prepare your body for corrective exercises. When I suggest you do a warm-up or a stretch twice, or 5 times, this means the number I've indicated is all you'll need to warm-up and stretch. It is only the exercises themselves that should be started slowly, doing only a few, and working up to 20 as your energy and endurance increase.

Warming up—exercise 1

2. Face the mirror. With your feet together, bring your arms over your head and put your palms together. Drop your head backward and hold. (See illustration.) Do this twice.

Warming up—exercise 2

3. Bend your knees, bend over and grasp your heels. (See illustration.) Raise your buttocks and straighten your legs. Do this twice.

Warming up—exercise 3

4. Raise hands over head, and, alternating arms, pretend to climb rope. (See illustration.) Repeat 5 times.

Warming up—exercise 4

Relax and shake your arms out before continuing your warm-up.

5. With your feet 3 feet apart, alternately slide your hands down the outside of your legs. (See illustration.) Repeat 10 times on each side.

Warming up—exercise 5

6. With your feet as far apart as possible, grasp the front of your thighs. (See illustrations.) Bend forward, making a flat back like a table. Move your hands down the back of your legs and grasp your heels. Try to touch your forehead to the floor. Do this twice.

Warming up—exercise 6

7. With your hands clasped behind your back at your shoulders and your legs apart, try to touch your head to the floor. Do this twice.

8. With your feet slightly apart and your arms outstretched in front of you, scissor your arms, working your shoulders and upper arms. Repeat 5 times.

9. With your arms outstretched at your sides and your hands closed in tight fists, start to make small circles with your arms; gradually increase the size of the circles. Then rotate, going from larger circles to smaller ones. Flex your hands and push outward with your palms. Shake out your hands. Do this twice. This is also a good execise for the upper arms.

10. With your hands on your hips and your legs slightly apart, rotate your head to loosen up your neck. Watch your head movement in the mirror to make sure you are making a complete circle as you rotate your head. Do this twice.

STRETCHING—DAILY ROUTINE

Each exercise should be done twice.

1. Sitting on the floor with your back straight, stretch out one leg and bring the other heel into the crotch area. (This stretches the

inner thigh.) Bring your hands over your head and climb rope. (See illustration.) Then bend down, and alternating, grasp your foot. Bring your chest down to your knee. (See illustration.) Don't tighten your neck or you'll get knots. Remember that all movements should be slow, graceful and progressive. This isn't a marathon race, and each exercise is designed to be easy and fun. (This exercise stretches the muscles of the buttocks, inner and outer thighs, and the calves.)

Stretching—exercise 1

2. Sitting on the floor with your legs as far apart as possible, put your hands on your knees. (See illustration.) Lean forward as far as you can and push down. (See illustration.) This stretches the lower back, chest and inner thighs. You can also feel it in your buttocks.

Stretching—exercise 2

3. For a complete stretch, lie flat on the floor with your legs slightly apart and your arms outstretched. Lean forward and grasp your feet. (See illustration.) If you can bend your elbows and put them on the floor, so much the better. Keep the backs of your knees flat and your back straight. Try to put your head between your legs. Do this once or twice.

Stretching—exercise 3

4. Kneel with your knees together and your ankles spread. Sit in between your legs, with your hands clasped behind your neck. Stretch the upper part of your feet. Lean backward and lower your body. (See illustration.) Feel the pressure in your lower back, then help yourself up with your elbows. (Don't try this one, however, if you have back problems.) On your knees, with your hands on the floor in front of you, straighten up and walk your feet up to your hands. Do this once or twice.

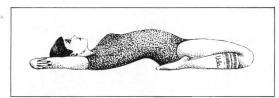

Stretching—exercise 4

5. Put your hands against the wall. With your pelvis tucked in, your buttocks and thigh muscles tight and your feet together, elevate 20 times. (See illustration.) When you feel your muscles start to burn, slow down.

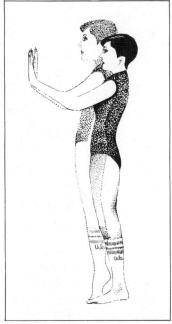

Stretching—exercise 5

6. Put your hands on the back of a chair or on a chest of drawers. Stand with your pelvis tucked in and your stomach and thighs tight, and place your right foot directly behind your left. With your heels on the floor, push in, pushing your hip forward. (See illustration.) Alternate feet. Do this exercise twice. (This exercise loosens up the hip joints.)

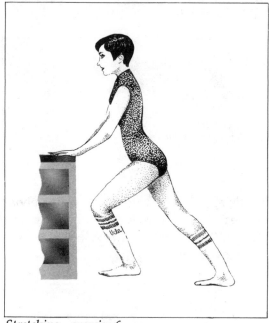

Stretching—exercise 6

In six minutes or less, you've stretched and warmed-up. That's not much time no matter how busy your life is.

FULL EXERCISES

Full exercises should be done only three times a week in the order I've specified here. Even when you are able to do each of them twenty times, the whole routine should take no more than an hour.

Thighs

1. Holding onto the back of a chair with your pelvis tucked forward and your knees straight, raise up on your toes and bend into a squat. (See illustration.) With your hips tucked forward as much as possible, still on your toes, sink into a sitting position on your calves and heels. Pull yourself up. Shake out your legs.

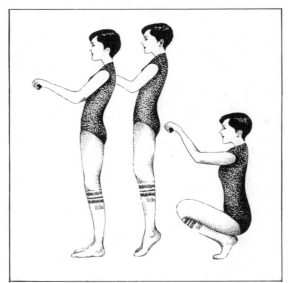

Thighs—exercise 1

2. In the same position, do the same exercise, raising and lowering yourself halfway.

3. Sitting on the floor, with your knees out as far as you can get them and the soles of your feet together and your back straight, grab your ankles. (See illustration.) Alternating, push your knees together while your hands (and elbows) are pushing out. (You can feel this in both your thighs and buttocks.)

Thighs—exercise 3

4. On your knees, with your knees separated and your arms outstretched in front of you, touch the floor, raise yourself and lean backward. (See illustration.)

Thighs—exercise 4

Legs and Waist

1. Lying on one hip, up on one elbow and supporting yourself with your other hand on the floor in front of you, raise your leg, keeping the movement smooth. (See illustration.) Alternate.

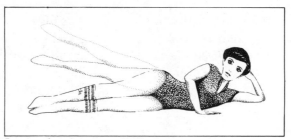

Legs and waist—exercise 1

2. Sit on your heels and stretch your arms forward. Rotate your buttocks from side to side. (See illustration.)

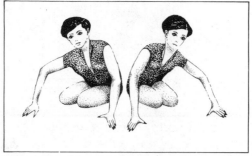

Legs and waist—exercise 2

Buttocks

1. Holding onto the back of a chair with your pelvis tucked in and your back straight, point your toe backward. (See illustration.) Raise your leg from the hip joint backward, keeping the toes pointed. Alternate and repeat.

Buttocks—exercise 1

2. On your knees, with your arms stretched forward, holding onto the arm of a chair, raise your leg behind you, pushing your leg backward. (See illustration.) Alternate legs and repeat.

Buttocks—exercise 2

Stomach

1. Lying on your back with your arms at your sides, the small of
   your back flat on the floor, your head back and your legs
   straight, scissor your legs up and then down. (See illustration.)
   When you feel tension, hold your legs in that position for a few
   seconds. (You will feel this exercise in your thighs, but it is actually to strengthen and firm your stomach muscles.)

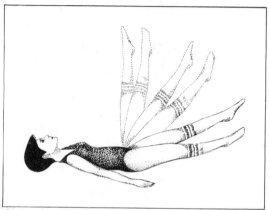

Stomach—exercise 1

2. Lie on your back with your knees toward the ceiling, feet flat
   against the floor. (See illustration.) Slowly, with your chin
   tucked against your chest, stretch your arms between your
   knees. Keep the small of your back flat against the floor and
   hold for a count of 5. (See illustration.) Slowly roll your spine
   against the floor and return to the starting position. Repeat.

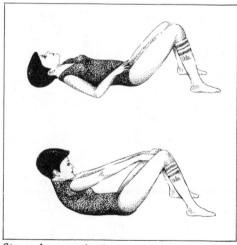

Stomach—exercise 2

Hip Joints

1. Lying on your back, pull your thighs to your chest. (See illustration.) Return to flat position and pull your right thigh to your chest. Again return to flat position and pull your left thigh to your chest. (See illustration.) Repeat entire sequence.

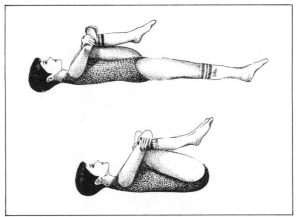

Hip joints—exercise 1

2. On your knees with your back straight and your hands on your hips, rotate the hips from left to right to left. (See illustration.) In the same position, make a circular motion with the hips.

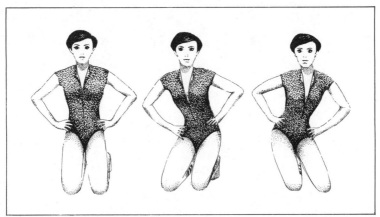

Hip joints—exercise 2

3. Lying on your stomach, with a beach ball between your feet, raise your legs and hold briefly.

This simple program, done regularly, will get you into great shape and keep you that way—with a minimum of effort.

7

What Your Hair Is All About

Each strand of hair consists of three layers. The outer layer, or cuticle, is made up of overlapping scales. The middle layer is made up of long thin cells. This is the layer that gives hair its elastic resilience and provides the pigment which gives hair its color. The innermost layer of spongy tissue has cells which occasionally contain granules of color pigment as well.

The part of the hair above the scalp is the shaft and the part beneath it is the root. Even if hair is pulled out by the "roots," The papilla is left behind. Eventually, the papilla manufactures and nurtures new hair. Because of this, plucking is never permanent. On the plus side, it is also the reason that hair loss due to abuse and breakage will eventually be replaced. Hair usually grows at the rate of one-half inch a month.

HOW WE ABUSE OUR HAIR

Tinting, bleaching, perming, straightening, long days in the sun all abuse the hair. Bleaching and straightening cause the most trouble. Other sources of hair abuse are the constant use of brush rollers, heated rollers, hot irons, pulling the hair when you're blowing it dry and elastic bands.

When we abuse our hair, we find ourselves with broken strands, split ends, hair that either looks greasy or dull and dry. If

135

split ends are not cut off, they will continue to split up the entire hair shaft. Dandruff, the most common of scalp disorders, can be caused by improper diet, sleeping in rollers, not brushing the hair, fatigue, climatic conditions and even emotional upset. If you find yourself with those unsightly white flakes on the shoulders of your smart new blazer, look first to your diet. A diet high in fats can aggravate the condition. It is also thought that sugar and starch are responsible. To see that the scalp is properly fed, lean meats, vegetables, salads and fresh fruit are recommended. The scalp should also be kept scrupulously clean. Use a medicated shampoo and shampoo daily, if necessary.

THE EASY WAY TO SHAMPOO

I always shampoo my hair while I take my shower so that I can be sure I get all the shampoo out of my hair, keeping in mind that it is the detergent in shampoo that is drying. Fashions in hair washing have changed over the years. Ten years ago, people only washed their hair every week or ten days. Shampoos developed then had to work hard. They had a high detergent content. Now that shampooing is an every third day, or even every other day, process, the milder shampoos with their lower detergent content that have been developed recently are all that is necessary.

I don't pour shampoo directly onto my hair. I always pour a tablespoon or so into my hands and work up a lather before applying it. Then I massage the shampoo into my scalp lightly with my fingertips and work out to the ends. I rinse my hair very well to get rid of the shampoo and its drying detergent. I pour a finishing rinse or quick conditioner into my hands and I apply it to my hair. It is the hair that needs conditioning, not the scalp.

A mild shampoo should state on the label that it has been sensitivity tested. It should cleanse the hair, but leave it receptive to conditioning. A conditioner restores bounce and body to the hair. It creates strength and flexibility. It replaces the moisture depleted by thermal and chemical processes.

A protein treatment can be used to condition the hair, especially if it is slightly damaged. Hair is 97 percent protein. Everything, from the sun, wind, blow drying, hot rollers and washing, removes the natural moisture and protein from the hair. A re-moisturizing cream can also be used as a conditioner. It replaces the moisture depleted by the thermal and chemical processes. It also restores body and bounce and creates strength and flexibility in the hair. It generates sheen and it moisturizes a dry, flaky scalp.

A finishing rinse untangles the hair, eliminates static electricity and texturizes the hair to make it more controllable.

I leave the quick conditioner or finishing rinse on my hair while I finish my shower. Then I rinse it away, making sure it has all been removed. I use a towel as a turban to soak up as much water as I can. Then I dry my hair very gently. I untangle my hair very gently with my fingers before I comb it with a wide-toothed comb.

Different types of hair require different degrees of care.

If Your Hair Is Dry and

. . . natural, which is to say not tinted, bleached, permed or straightened, choose a shampoo for dry hair, and follow with a cream finishing rinse. Use a deep conditioning treatment every three weeks.

. . . tinted, permed or straightened, overexposed to the sun or chlorine, with split ends, choose a shampoo for tinted or dry hair and a cream finishing rinse. Use a quick conditioner once a week, and give your hair a deep conditioning treatment every three weeks.

. . . bleached and lightened, choose a shampoo for lightened hair and a cream finishing rinse. Use a quick conditioner once a week, and a deep conditioning treatment every three weeks.

If Your Hair Is Oily and

. . . natural, which is to say not tinted, bleached, permed or straightened, choose a shampoo for oily hair and an astringent rinse. Give your hair a deep conditioning treatment once a month. Shampoo often.

. . . tinted, permed or straightened, overexposed to the sun or chlorine, with split ends, choose a shampoo for tinted or oily hair. Use a quick conditioner every two weeks. Give your hair a deep conditioning treatment every month.

. . . bleached or lightened, choose a shampoo for lightened hair. Use a quick conditioner every week. Give your hair a deep conditioning treatment every month.

If Your Hair Is Normal and

. . . natural, which is to say not tinted, bleached, permed or straightened, choose a mild shampoo and a natural rinse. Give your hair a deep conditioning treatment once a month.

. . . tinted, permed or straightened, overexposed to the sun or chlorine, with problem split ends, choose a shampoo for tinted hair. Use a quick conditioner every two weeks, and give your hair a deep conditioning treatment once a month.

. . . bleached or lightened, choose a shampoo for lightened hair. Use a quick conditioner once a week, and a deep conditioning treatment once a month.

HOW TO DRY YOUR HAIR

Because my hair is short, by the time I have finished my morning health and beauty maintenance program, dealt with the kids, and am ready to start my day, it is dry. It also looks the very best it can because it is well cut and conditioned properly.

Just letting your hair dry in the air is one way, but only one. A hot comb also works for short, off-the-face hair, and so does a hand-held blow dryer, which, if it is not the greatest invention since Saran Wrap, still rates high on my list of aids to a busy, active life. When my hair was long, I always used a hand-held blow dryer to both dry and shape it. Here is my method:

Drying

Using a wide-toothed comb, I divide my hair into six sections, one on each side of my face, two on the back of my head, and two on the top. Holding the dryer six inches away from my hair, I keep it in constant motion. I start at one side of my face and work around, drying the front section last.

Once I have used a wide-tooth comb, I switch to a brush to pick up the hair layer by layer as I dry it. When one section of my hair is dry, I bring it down, layer by layer, and move on to the next.

Shaping

If I want to turn the ends of my hair under, I twirl them under with the brush and use the blow dryer, going all around my head as I did when my hair was wet. Then I fluff it up a bit with the brush. It can help if there is some way you can see the back of your head. If necessary, use your makeup mirror. A woman can be perfectly combed from the front, but when she turns around her hair may be flat in the back. Be sure the back of your hair looks as good as the front.

Another method for drying long hair is to let it dry, put it into a ponytail, and then divide it into four sections that go on electric rollers for five minutes.

PICKING THE RIGHT HAIRBRUSH

Brushing is not only easier on your hair than combing, it also helps to get rid of accumulated dust as it distributes natural scalp oils evenly through the hair.

Just as there are different types of hair, there are also different types and styles of hairbrushes. One difference is in the type of bristles. There are natural and synthetic bristles. Fine hair should be brushed with a soft-bristle brush, which usually means a natural bristle brush. Medium textured hair needs a stiffer bristle, which can either mean a natural or a synthetic bristle. Coarse hair needs a very stiff bristle, which usually means a synthetic bristle. When you're buying a brush, be sure the bristles aren't sharp. A sharp bristle can cause damage to the hair cuticles. Instead, look for a brush with rounded or blunt bristle ends.

After you've picked your bristle type, you'll then need to select a shape. Brushes come in round or half-round, oval or rectangular shapes. The type of brush you pick will be determined by the way you brush your hair. If you flick your wrist at the end of each stroke, a full-round or half-round brush will take the advantage of that stroke. If you brush in an up and down motion and if you have long hair, select a flat oval brush for its brushing surface. If your hair is short, look for a flat brush that is narrow and rectangular.

The Right Way to Brush

Bend forward so your hair hangs down in front of your face. Start at the ends of the hair, gradually taking longer and longer strokes until you're brushing from the scalp. Loosen tangles with your fingers, and continue brushing.

If you brush too hard or too long, you can cause excess hair loss or tear your hair. Any manipulation of the hair stimulates the oil glands of the scalp, so too much brushing can make your hair more oily. I find twenty-five strokes a day is right for me. And don't brush your hair when it's wet. Wet hair is stretched out to its full length, and, like a stretched-out rubber band, it has lost its natural elasticity and strength. Brushing wet hair can cause splits and cracks over the entire hair shaft. When your hair is wet, use a wide-toothed comb to untangle it, starting at the ends of the hair and gradually working up toward the scalp.

Caring for Your Brush

Wash your brush every time you wash your hair, first removing old hairs with a comb. Swish your brush gently in tepid soapy water. Don't use harsh detergents and don't soak the brush, which loosens the bristles. Rinse in lukewarm water, then cold, and shake off the excess moisture. Your brush should never be dried over a radiator or other heat source. Just put it on the sink and let it dry, bristle-side down.

HOW TO MAKE THE MOST OF THE COLOR OF YOUR HAIR

After you have the perfect wash-and-wear haircut, color is the most becoming change you can make to your hair. I'm not talking about changing your own shade. A color conditioner that matches your own hair color exactly will give your hair sheen, new body and new highlights.

All you have to do is turn on the television and you'll see the variety of hair coloring products that have been developed for use at home. One glorious creature after another rides her horse or drives her Ferrari or glides through a field of daisies, each extolling the virtues of whatever hair coloring product she is supposedly using. My own opinion is that a temporary rinse is the only coloring agent the nonprofessional should try to use at home. If you try to make extreme color changes at home, it is the equivalent of trying to operate on yourself for appendicitis. Having your hair colored professionally is going to cost you money. In my opinion, it is money well spent.

There are three different coloring agents.

The Temporary Rinse

A temporary coloring agent is the rinse which can be used easily at home with good results. A rinse coats the hair shaft with clear color to darken or highlight it. On light-to-medium-colored hair, a rinse will add gold or copper highlights, heighten the red in the hair or tone it down. Rinses work well as toners on hair that has been professionally colored and that has oxidized to an ugly shade. A rinse will also help to tone gray hair. Because a rinse does not contain bleach, it won't lighten your hair.

The rinse you use should have built-in conditioners. A rinse does not penetrate the hair shaft, so there is no possibility of damage, and it will wash away with your next shampoo. If you are planning to have a permanent, even mild coloring like a rinse should not be used. Any coloring should be used two weeks after a permanent.

Semipermanent Coloring

Semipermanent coloring does what a rinse does, only more so. It does change the hair structure slightly by penetrating the hair shaft as well as coating it. A bit of the semipermanent color is washed away each time you shampoo. You can hasten the departure of a semipermanent color you don't like by shampooing often.

Permanent Coloring

Using bleach, tint or dye, a permanent hair color alters the structure of your hair. The important thing to remember is that whatever color you and your colorist choose, it must suit the tone of your skin and the color of your eyes. Hair coloring has become very sophisticated since the days of a flat, all-one hair color. The colorist now mixes up to a dozen separate tints to use on a single head of hair so that enough of your natural shading remains to flatter your complexion.

Henna

If the notion of using henna brings to your mind a picture of your Great Aunt Sal with her bright orange hair, that's not the way things are anymore. Henna on almost black hair can make it gleam and glow. Henna on drab brown hair can bring the color bouncing to the surface. Henna is popular again, and with good reason.

If you decide to make a radical change in the color of your hair, be prepared for the continuing care it is going to need. You will need frequent touch-ups and treatment to keep your new hair color perfect, shiny and beautiful.

SHOPPING FOR A HAIRDRESSER

Your hair is not going to look its best unless it is cut in a style that flatters the shape of your face. It should also be cut in a style that fits the way you live and reflects the way you see yourself. No matter how good you feel in the morning, you're not going to be able to say that you've done the very best with what you have if you look into the mirror and see your face framed by an unbecoming hair style.

You wouldn't think of going to a doctor or a dentist who hasn't been highly recommended. I think the same standards should apply when you shop for a hairdresser. Hairdressers can be intimidating. They are among the few professionals, along with doctors, dentists and manicurists, who can put their hands on you. A hairdresser can make you look different and feel different about yourself, and not necessarily for the better. We can all count the times we've walked out of a beauty shop in tears. The person who cuts your hair must be someone with whom you can communicate. Otherwise, it can be a disaster.

Shop around to find the right hairdresser. One way to get a start is to ask a friend whose haircut you admire where she has it done. Even a stranger on the street or in an elevator will be flattered if you ask her where she has her hair done. You wouldn't ask if you didn't admire the great way she looks.

If you don't see any haircuts around that really appeal to you, another way to find the right hairdresser is to go directly to the source. Go into a salon that catches your eye, and tell the receptionist that you're shopping for a hairdresser. A good salon will understand that this particular quest is no minor matter. After all, when a client walks out looking as good as she can possibly look, it is an advertisement for their excellence. A good salon will be delighted to offer a prospective client a place to sit and perhaps a cup of coffee to make the experience a pleasant one as she gets the feel of the various stylists.

As you watch the way the stylists move around the chair, the rapport they have with their clients and especially the way those clients look when they are ready to walk out the door to face the world, there will be one or two stylists to whom you are drawn. When the stylist you think is the one for you has a break, walk up, introduce yourself and say that you're thinking about a change and that you are impressed with his or her work. Think about how you would feel as somebody approached you to tell you that they admired what you are doing. Wouldn't you be pleased and flattered? So will a stylist.

You've had the experience where you've walked into a salon for the first time and somebody has grabbed you, stuffed you into a robe and washed your hair. When the stylist sees you for the first time, what stands in front of him or her is an anonymous, robed creature who could be any size or shape with stringy, wet hair. I believe the first time you meet your stylist, you should give him or her the clearest possible picture of who you are and how you see yourself. The way your hair is cut must fit not only the contours of your face, but it must also be in balance with your height and weight. The way you dress should give the stylist additional information about the way you live and how you want to look. If you are wearing tight jeans and boots, he or she will get a different message than if you were wearing a soft dress and delicate sandals.

I think most hairdressers are aware of the power they have over their clients. They know that when a woman walks into a salon to have her hair cut, she wants to walk out looking good, with a style that fits the way she lives. Remember those days not so long ago when a visit to a beauty salon meant a half-day commitment every week? There we all were, docile little sheep, with our hair set in elaborate combinations and permutations of rollers and pins, spending hours frying our scalps and ears under the dryer. I used to be there, too, with my beehive and my backcombing, with the back of my hair cut like a football player's helmet. Not only do I believe that a too-elaborate hair style looks old-fashioned these days, but with the busy lives most women have, nobody has the time for a time-consuming hair care regime. We need our time for more important things.

What works best for me is a haircut that is short, but still flattering, what I call a ''wash-and-wear'' haircut. Your haircut can be longer, of course. The goal is to have a haircut that can be taken care of at home. Not only does this save both time and money, but it looks better. It looks vital and modern, and it fits into the busy lives that women lead today.

Any hairdresser, unless he has Nancy Reagan in the chair preparing her for Prince Charles's wedding, will be willing to take a look at a prospective client and give her a free consultation. If you agree with what the stylist has in mind, there's no time like the present to act. If the stylist isn't free, make an appointment for another time.

WHAT THE RIGHT HAIRCUT CAN DO FOR YOU

If Your Face Is Too Round

Because the hair has volume, a fuller haircut will help to minimize the size of the face and can give it the illusion of correcting its shape.

If Your Face Is Too Long

Bangs will help to minimize the length of your face. The face can be divided into three parts, starting with the hairline to the brow, the eyebrows to the upper lip and from the upper lip to the chin. If you cover the top, the remaining two-thirds make the face seem shorter.

If Your Nose Is Too Big

If your nose is quite impossible, you might want to consider plastic surgery. Before you do that, consult with your hairdresser who may recommend a hairdo that is a bit higher. Balance is the solution.

If Your Jaw Is Too Square

A square jaw is definitely a matter for your hairdresser. He may suggest a marvelous pageboy cut. When your hair swings forward, it will hit right at the jawline, which will minimize it.

WHAT ABOUT WIGS?

At a time when every woman wants a healthy, glowing, natural look, it may seem somewhat of an anachronism to even talk about wigs, which could well be in the heaven reserved for fashions past, along with the corset and false eyelashes. There are times, though, when I think a good wig is just what you need to make the very most of what you have.

For example, you are on a business trip and you know you won't have the time to get to a hairdresser so that you will look your very best for your meeting. Take along your wig and this problem is solved.

You are on vacation in a tropical climate where most of your day is spent in the hotel swimming pool or scuba diving. What do you do when the cocktail hour arrives and you want to present a cool, fresh, glowing, perfect look? Take along your wig and this problem is solved.

You are invited to the party of the year. You want your hair to look as dramatic as your new red gown with the spaghetti straps and the sides slashed to the knee to show off your glittering stockings and delicate evening sandals. I think an elegant evening party calls for a face with a little more dash to it. I put gold glitter on my eyelids and even on my lips. Why not a little more dash to your hair as well? Women are fulfilling so many roles these days. We are out in the business world, we are wives, mothers, daughters, friends, neighbors, lovers. Where is it written that we can't on occasion look as glamorous as the sirens of old? Wear a wig, and knock them dead.

What Kind of a Wig?

If you have problems with hair loss or if your hair is just so thin and fine that there is no way it can ever please you, this might be the time to invest in a high-quality wig of human hair. If, on the other hand, you will be wearing a wig only on occasion, a good synthetic wig looks right and feels right.

You wouldn't buy an expensive Galanos gown without looking at it from every angle to be sure it is right for you. It is just as important to take equal care when selecting a wig. Here are a few basic rules.

It has to fit. You don't want to feel that your head is caught in a vise when you're wearing a wig, but it should be able to withstand a saucy toss of the head without ending up in your soup. There is a happy medium where your wig will look as natural as your own hair. Cast a critical eye at yourself to be sure you've hit it.

As with any hair color, remember that the color of your wig must suit the color of your eyes and skin.

Your wig salesperson will show you how to wear a wig properly. To keep it clean, it should be brushed. Most wigs come with washing instructions. If you follow them, your wig will look as shiny and bouncy as your own hair.

Wearing a wig for more than five or six hours is bad for the hair and scalp. Even a lightweight wig will make your scalp perspire. Take your wig off after this time to let your hair and scalp breathe.

WHAT TO DO ABOUT UNWANTED HAIR

It's a woman's glory when it is properly on our heads. On our legs, arms, underarms, faces, and at our bikini lines it qualifies as unwanted hair. Because shaving under the arms has to be done nearly every day, I just use an inexpensive razor and a watchful eye. For my legs, forearms and, in the summer, my bikini line, I go to a salon to have unwanted hair removed by waxing. There are, however, several excellent ways to deal with unwanted hair.

Depilatories

Chemical depilatories, which come in powder, gel, cream or spray form, soften and dissolve the hair shaft. The root is not affected and it does grow back. Over a period of time, the use of depilatories slows hair growth. When the hair does grow back, it does so more slowly and often less noticeably.

Electrolysis

In electrolysis, a fine wire needle is introduced into the opening of the hair follicle. An electric current is transmitted down the needle to destroy the papilla. There are no scars and hair from that particular papilla should never grow again. Electrolysis is expensive, but for some people, it is money well spent. If there is a hint of a mustache on your upper lip, electrolysis is the answer. If your eyebrows grow too closely together over your nose, or if they are bushy and unflattering to your face, electrolysis is the answer. It is also often used to remove hairs growing around the nipples.

Shaving

The quickest, easiest and least expensive way to remove unwanted hair is to shave. It does have its drawbacks. You are left with a stubble buildup, and shaving has to be done frequently. If you use an electric razor to shave, once a week before your bath use a lot of pre-electric shave conditioner on whatever area you plan to shave. After shaving, wash off all the pre-electric shave conditioner and rinse thoroughly. After your bath, moisturize the areas you have shaved with a lavish amount of body lotion.

If you shave with a safety razor, once a week when you are just out of your bath, rub lots of moisturizing lotion all over the areas you want to shave. Then coat them with shaving foam. Let it set for 60 seconds and then shave. Rinse thoroughly in warm, running water. After you are dry, moisturize thoroughly.

Tweezing

Tweezing is the way to get rid of those occasional hairs that ruin the arch of your eyebrows. If you do it properly, it can be relatively painless, especially if you anesthetize the brows first with ice. Using a magnifying mirror, brush your eyebrows up into the arch you want. Tweeze one hair at a time in the direction in which it grows. Always thin from below the brow line. Do one brow at a time. When both are symmetrical, saturate a cotton pad with disinfectant or alcohol and wipe your brows. Be careful not to let any of the liquid run into your eyes.

Waxing

With this method, a thin layer of melted wax is applied to the skin. It is allowed to cool and then quickly stripped off, which tears the hair out with it. Because the hair has been torn out from below the surface of the skin, it takes a long time before the new hairs begin to show. There is no regrowth stubble. As with depilatories, waxing, in time, also retards the regrowth of new hair. Waxing is not painless, but it is the method I prefer. Although I go to a salon to have my legs, arms and bikini line waxed, you can also buy a waxing kit at your drugstore. These are very good products which can easily be used at home.

8

What Your Skin Is All About

If I am caught by the way somebody moves, by the way somebody looks, I am actually watching their skin. Your skin has no place to hide. It is the wrapping on the package. At Christmas a couple of years ago, I received a package from a department store in Texas celebrated for its exquisite gift wrapping. I couldn't wait to get it open. Off came the silver bells and the silver ribbon, the marvelous paper. Inside the box was nothing but tissue paper. Somehow, whatever was to be included in the package had been left out.

Wouldn't it be wonderful if it were possible for the wrapping on our package, for our skin, to look as beautiful as that package did with no visible means of support? For skin to look its best, though, it must be fed by a nutritious diet, and given fresh air, exercise and a proper amount of sleep. Skin needs to be kept very clean. We must develop skin awareness. It reflects what we eat, how we take care of ourselves, our every mood, our health and the level of our self-esteem.

Skin is the largest organ system of the body, comprising 16 to 18 percent of our body weight. It has four functions:

1. It protects the body from mechanical and radiation injuries.
2. It is a sense organ.
3. It regulates temperature.
4. It metabolizes and stores fat.

149

The protective epidermis that we see is separated from the nourishing dermis below. The dermis manufactures new cells rapidly, transmitting them from the lower to the upper level in a little over fifteen days. If you eat properly, drink plenty of water, exercise and keep your skin clean, in only a little over fifteen days, your skin will look glowing and new. The dermis is packed with oil glands, hair follicles, blood vessels, nerve tissue and sweat glands. Collagen and elastin are both major proteins and building blocks of the dermis layer of the skin. It is the collagen fibers in the connective tissue of the skin which undergo changes with aging and overexposure to the sun, and contribute to the appearance of wrinkles and other outward signs of age. Elastin is an albuminoid that forms the chief constituent of elastic fibers. Any successful skin care program must consider the separate needs and reactions of both epidermis and dermis.

When skin looks smooth, glowing and healthy, it reflects its natural moisture. Think about when you just step out of your warm bath or shower. Your skin cells are plump because they are moist. Sealing in that natural moisture with a moisturizer will keep it that way, at least temporarily. Women have told me that they've stepped from their bath or shower with skin looking so smooth and firm that they haven't bothered with their moisturizer. In less than an hour, they tell me, their skin looks like Margo's in *Lost Horizon* after she left Shangri-la. Without a moisturizer to seal it in, the natural moisture of the skin evaporates in about twenty minutes.

There is a second reason for using a moisturizer. The minute we walk outside, our skin is exposed to all types of environmental pollution, to the bite of winter's cold, to the drying sun. Inside, our skin is exposed to air conditioning, which sucks the moisture out of the skin, as does heat, fluorescent lights, cigarette smoke, the stress and pressure of the day. Even the wash-and-wear products we put on can irritate the skin. Moisturizing the skin not only keeps the good things in, it also keeps the bad things out.

Any beauty and health care program must be fast, easy and fun, or nobody is going to do it. If you have a late night with too much wine, if you don't exercise for a couple of weeks, if you succumb to a yearning for that perfect chocolate soufflé, the world isn't going to come to an end. There is always tomorrow. Not so with skin care. It's the one area of beauty and health care that I believe should be followed diligently, no matter how late the night, no matter what the level of fatigue. We have to get tough with ourselves about our skin.

Proper skin care will help it to obtain its own equilibrium and protect it against the loss of its essential elements. When I began to do my research on the skin, I found that I was taking proper care of my skin. I had been doing it all along without realizing it. I keep to a diligent skin care program so that when I'm fifty-five or sixty or older, I won't have to make up for what I haven't done. It pays off. Every time I see a woman like Aida Grey or Estee Lauder, who has devoted her life to skin care, I see that she practices what she preaches. Both of these women have a marvelous glow.

All kinds of products have been developed by the major cosmetics companies to help us with a skin care program. Rather than just coming out with one item, most of them come out with a line of three or four products. This is not just to fill up your shopping bags. These products have been developed to interact chemically to provide maximum benefit for your skin.

That is where you come in. You have to experiment with the various products to find out what each of them does for you. Picking the smallest size, try a moisturizer from one line, and a toner from another, a cleansing cream from one, and an eye cream from another. It's essentially trial and error until you find out the right combination. What you have to do is listen to what your skin is saying. It won't be a shout; it will be a whisper. When you find the combination of products appropriate to your own skin type, you will be aware of subtle differences in your skin. One combination will conserve moisture, maintain suppleness, encourage a fine texture and soften the superficial lines that might otherwise turn into wrinkles.

DETERMINING YOUR SKIN TYPE

The first step in constructing an easy program of skin care is to find out your individual skin type. Here are the possibilities:

Normal Skin

No skin is normal all the time. For most people, there are times when the skin is either dry or oily, sometimes at the same time. The skin is continually being fed from inside the body and the oil produced by the sebaceous glands lubricates the pores no matter what the skin type. At times when the skin is normal, the pores are not clogged with oil, and there are no eruptions.

Dry Skin

Dry skin is characterized by small white flakes, occasional patchy red areas and tautness. Often the permanent lines running from each side of the nose to the corners of the mouth seem deeper than average.

Oily Skin

Oily skin is characterized by large pores and blemishes. Although a proper cleansing program is never going to reduce the size of the pores, it can bring oily skin under control and into balance for a clean, clear, blemish-free complexion.

Combination Skin

Sometimes the sebaceous glands around the nose, mouth, chin and forehead are a little overactive because of a change of climate, water or stress. When this happens, these areas of the face are oily while the rest of the face is dry. This condition can also be brought under control and balanced by a proper program of skin care.

YOUR SKIN AND DIET

A wholesome diet is essential to proper skin care. We've all heard the benefits of lean meat, fish, poultry, eggs, fresh vegetables and fruits. Add specific items like avocado, cucumbers and cabbage to your list. Vitamins and minerals are crucial to a healthy skin; and the foods that provide them are:

Vitamin A

Found in yellow and green vegetables and fish, Vitamin A helps to prevent acne.

Vitamin C

Found abundantly in oranges and other citrus fruits, Vitamin C is crucial to the formation of collagen and elastin, both major proteins and building blocks of the dermis layer of the skin.

Vitamin K

Found in red meat, egg yolks and green vegetables, Vitamin K aids the proper synthesis of the clotting factor in the bloodstream and prevents bruising.

Iron

Iron is found in red meats, liver, kidneys and leafy green vegetables. An iron deficiency can lead to hair loss and an uncomfortably dry skin.

Amino Acids

Without the protein building blocks called amino acids, the skin will stretch and droop. It won't heal properly and it will wrinkle early. Amino acids are found in milk, meat, fish, poultry, eggs and fresh fruits and vegetables.

Fatty acids insure the metabolism of the skin, which is the process of building and shedding cells at the right speed in the right amounts. The oiliness of the skin is not affected by the fat in the diet, but rather by the hormone level in the bloodstream.

The hormone balance is responsible for the coarsening of pores at puberty. It is the sex hormones that stimulate the sebaceous glands. They enlarge and so do the ducts and pores they feed. Too much stimulation of the sebaceous glands leads to acne, one of several skin diseases involving the oil glands and hair follicles, which are marked by inflamed pustules or pimples. Years ago, eating chocolate was blamed for acne. Subsequent research has shown that, although fatty acids can aggravate acne, diet plays very little part in its appearance. Scrupulous cleanliness in mild cases helps, and a physician may prescribe a mild antibiotic, such as tetracycline, as a solution in more serious cases.

DON'TS FOR YOUR SKIN

Androgen is a sex-related hormone which causes pimples by stimulating the skin's oil glands to excessive oil secretion. If a tendency toward pimples is a problem for you, there are some naturally androgenic foods you should avoid, although they can be beneficial as sources of protein, vitamins and minerals. They are (1) wheat germ, (2) shellfish and (3) organ meats, such as liver and kidneys. Androgen-free foods, such as pork, lamb and fish, are all good sources of protein during those times when you have an outbreak of pimples.

Beware of blushing foods, such as chili, curry, and hot peppers, as well as the caffeine in coffee and tea and the alcohol in wine and liquor. All cause vasodilation, which is the expansion of the blood vessels.

Beware of a dangerously low calorie level. You must eat a

proper diet. If you don't weigh enough, not only will your health obviously suffer, but your skin will look dull and aged.

Beware of obesity. Too much fat makes an individual prone to eczema and fungal infections. Because overweight people perspire too much, it fouls up the body's own systems of self-disinfection. The heavy person is an easy target for skin irritation and infection.

Beware of overdoing high cholesterol foods such as milk, beef and butter. They can cause fatty tumors.

COMMON SKIN PROBLEMS

Pseudo-Wrinkles

Some wrinkles are permanent and some, fortunately, aren't. Only the deft hand of the plastic surgeon will banish permanent wrinkles, but nonpermanent wrinkles are nothing more than the dehydration of the skin. There are several major causes of pseudo-wrinkling.

Sun

A good tan says a lot about you. It says that you have the leisure to spend your time in the sun getting brown. It puts you on the beach with those lazy beauties in the slick magazines who advertise Caribbean holidays. But, let's face it, the sun is not good for us in large doses. I agree that a hint of color in the face looks marvelous. It says health and sparkle. But the sun also dehydrates the skin. It causes permanent, irreversible damage to the skin by aging it, blistering it, drying it, blotching it. The sun is one of the reasons for those broken capillaries on your cheeks. It can even cause skin cancer. Protection is paramount. Shun the sun when you can. When you are out in the sun, use a good moisturizing sun block to protect your skin. Ten minutes a day is enough time in the sun when you are starting to work on your tan. The hours between eleven in the morning and two in the afternoon are those when the rays of the sun are at their strongest and, therefore, their most damaging. Program your time in the sun before eleven in the morning or after two in the afternoon.

While a good moisturizing sun block, an ingredient of every commercial suntan lotion, can help to protect the natural moisture of the skin, what is lost during your time in the sun can be restored by taking a lukewarm bath. Hot water is bad for the skin, which you might remember the next time you're tempted to try a hot tub. It opens the pores and the moisture escapes. Just think about the last time you lolled around for hours in a hot bath. Remember how your fingertips looked when you got out? They looked as if they should be on the hands of the two-thousand-year-old woman, didn't they?

What happens to your fingertips in a hot bath is also happening to the skin on the rest of your body. A lukewarm bath, though, will restore the moisture to your skin. If you fill your tub with bubble bath, you might as well plop the laundry into the tub, too. It's like filling it with detergent. Instead, add a few tablespoons of peanut, olive, vegetable or baby oil to your bath. I also use either a couple of drops of Vitamin E oil or a few tablespoons of unscented sesame seed oil. I love to luxuriate in the bathtub, but I never forget that a hot bath is no friend of mine.

When you get out of the bath, moisturize. Body lotion is to texturize the dry, flaky skin. It also plumps up the skin. Because the point of body lotion is to seal in the moisture, I moisturize when I am barely dry. There are many good creams and lotions to use on your body. I prefer to use a cream. Lotions are for those with oilier skin.

Acne Medication

Many medications prescribed for acne contain drying agents, such as sulfur, resorcinol, or alcohol. If you must use such medication and you find it drying to your skin, ask your doctor to prescribe something else, or cut down on the medication to see if it works just as well with less of it.

Water Pills

The two groups that take water pills seem to be younger people who use them as a diuretic to shed water weight, or older people who take them upon the prescription of their doctors for medical problems. Younger people who take water pills and find that they cause dehydration of the skin can just stop taking them. Older people can use oils and creams to compensate for water loss.

Sudden Weight Loss

Acute, sudden weight loss through crash diets doesn't give the body a chance to fill in the skin with collagen, elastin and the other elements of dermal tissue. Weight should be lost slowly or your skin will suffer.

Blemishes

The facial skin is an extension of the scalp. If you have a dry, flaky scalp, most of the time you will have dry, flaky patches on your face. If you have an oily scalp, the chances are that you will also have an oily skin with the accompanying large pores and a tendency to break out. If your skin is dry and flaky, there are creams to replenish its natural oils and to help it in its exchange of oxygen and carbon dioxide. If your skin is oily, there are products on the market to balance the moisture in oily skin and retard its breakthrough of excess oil. A blend of the right emollients and a complex of moisture-retaining elements will protect the skin without oily buildup.

There is no such thing as a hypoallergenic product. There are only products with fewer irritants, which are also always fragrance free. Perfumed products smell good, but they're drying to the skin. I know women who feel as if they are treating themselves to a luxury when they wash their faces with a perfumed soap. Although there is nothing that gets the face cleaner than soap, one of the cardinal rules of cleansing your face is to see that the cleansing agent is all washed off. What of a perfumed soap then? It's all gone. Save the perfumed soaps for the guest bathroom, or take off the wrappers and put the soap in with your lingerie or sweaters.

Even if we spend our days doing nothing but lounging on a chaise, petting the poodle and reading Kafka, we still lose 3 quarts of water a day. That's why it is so important to drink a lot of water. It keeps the system hydrated. I keep a pitcher of water beside my bed at night. On airplanes, I drink a lot of water. And, if I'm not rushing right from the airport to a lecture or a television appearance, I never wear makeup when I fly. I carry a plastic bottle of Evian water and spray my face regularly.

Even when proper skin care has become as much of a daily habit as brushing your teeth morning and night, you still might find you have blemishes. Some of the common ones and how to deal with them are:

Acne

Acne is the curse of the adolescent. Years ago, it was thought that a junk food diet caused acne. In those pre-McDonald's days, it was the corner malt shop, and especially the chocolate malts, that got the blame. Would that it were so. In fact, diet has little to do with acne. It is the sex hormones that cause it, and because the sex hormones are at their most active during adolescence as they reach their balance, acne is the visible evidence.

With acne, iron discipline must be evoked to keep the skin clean at all times. Your dermatologist might prescribe a peeling agent to hasten the departure of the old layer of skin, or he might prescribe a low-level antibiotic, such as tetracycline, which seems to help.

At my lectures, there always seem to be a few women who had skin like a baby until they were in their twenties. They were the fortunate few who escaped teen-age acne entirely. It is sad to see a lovely woman who has learned to take care of herself and yet still wakes in the morning to see acne eruptions on her face. At this point, acne is a matter for her and her dermatologist. Very possibly, he might advise skin peeling as a way to banish the old layer of skin and start all over again.

Blackheads

Blackheads, the most common form of skin blemish, are oil plugs that turn black upon contact with the air. A proper cleansing program keeps them from appearing. If they do persist, use hot compresses on your face to open the pores. Then, using the fingertips and not the nails, remove them. When you have completed this process, wash, tone and moisturize. Whiteheads should be treated in the same way.

Dermatitis

This catch-all phrase refers to inflammations of the skin that can be caused by physical or emotional stress. Your dermatologist will be able to control the symptoms, but not the cause.

Pigment Blotches

Removing pigment blotches acquired by too much sun or reportedly as a side effect of the Pill is not easy. There are bleach creams on the market, but many are too harsh to be safe. Again, this is a topic to discuss with your dermatologist.

Warts and Moles

Again, see your dermatologist.

Broken Veins

Those awful, spidery capillaries that appear on the cheeks and the legs are the hardest to deal with. They can be caused by too much sun or by changes of temperature. They can be caused by the caffeine in coffee, tea and soft drinks. They can be caused by too much smoking. The only way to remove them is to have your dermatologist drain them with a needle developed for the purpose, which can leave tiny scars, or to have him freeze them away.

FACING UP TO THE WEATHER

Winter

I love winter. I love putting on tweeds and heavy jackets, winding long woolly scarves around my neck. To me, the onset of the New Year is a time of looking back and evaluating the year just past, of looking ahead over the ring of crystal champagne glasses to the challenges of the year ahead. And, if I'm just tramping along on a cold day, I love the feel of the cold against my cheeks, love the sight of my breath.

I know, though, that winter doesn't love my skin. During the winter months I double the protection of my skin. The outdoors, though stimulating and vigorous, turns skin dry and flaky. Inside a heated house, office or department store, the artificial heating sucks the moisture from the skin, drying and dehydrating it.

Foundation, along with moisturizer, helps to protect the skin against the elements. Never leave the house without it. Winter is also the time to use an eye cream during the day. If you live in an area where the water is hard, remember that hard water is also drying to the skin, another reason to be sure your skin is protected by moisturizer, foundation and eye cream just as you protect yourself against the cold with mufflers, big coats, knitted caps and boots.

Take lukewarm showers rather than baths and make them short. Buy a humidifier or fill your living space with plants to help to humidify the dry air.

I've found the best makeup to wear in cold weather is moisture rich and waterproof, and even in the winter, I never forget that the sun still presents a hazard to my skin, especially when its effects are augmented by wind or snow. On cloudy or hazy days, up to 80 percent of the sun's ultraviolet rays still reach the earth's surface. On snowy, sunny days, skin can still be burned by ultraviolet light reflected from the snow. The doctors I have spoken to encourage the use of a broad-spectrum sunscreen year round on all exposed skin.

Wind, as it blows across the skin's surface, causes water loss through evaporation. That's why strong wind, whether it feels hot and humid or dry and cold, affects your skin in any climate. In the cold, wind accelerates moisture loss. Foundation, moisturizer and an eye cream (the area around the eyes is the driest part of the body) will help you to fight the effects of a windy day.

Spring

Spring, with its blossoms and promises, gives skin a needed breathing spell between the hazards of winter's chill and summer's sun. It's the time to go back to leisurely baths, to use an eye cream only at night, to cut down on your foundation both inside and outside your home or office.

Still, the days of spring can be cloudy or hazy, or a strong wind can be blowing. If the day is cloudy or hazy, remember to use your sunscreen on all exposed skin. If it is windy, use a rich moisturizer and an eye cream to protect against water loss through evaporation.

Spring is also the time to think ahead to lazy days on the beach in a tiny bikini. Plan ahead by starting on *The Fast, Easy, Fun Way to a Body Shape That Is As Good As It Can Be* (p. 119), and start to get your body back in shape with *The Golden Door's Virtue-Making Diet* (p. 114). Spring is the time to start the day with a few deep breaths to get the oxygen coursing through your veins, to walk briskly as you go about the demands of your busy day.

Summer

During the summer, we have to prepare not only for the heat and humidity of the outdoors, but for the air conditioning indoors that sucks the moisture out of our skin. Because we perspire, our pores are clogged under our moisturizer and foundation. The air conditioning dries the skin. Summer is the time to be doubly conscientious about keeping the skin clean. Perhaps it would be best to cleanse, tone and moisturize more than twice a day.

We know that hot water opens the pores, allowing the skin's natural moisture to escape. Well, cold water has the opposite effect. Cold water closes the pores, which seals in the moisture. Washing with cold water in the winter gives the skin a tight, dry, uncomfortable feeling. But in the summer, I find that nothing feels better than splashing my face with cold water. I also find it refreshing to splash cold water on my wrists and the back of my neck. This reduces the body temperature, and makes me feel more energetic on a broiling, humid day.

Another problem of summer, especially in a city where the water is soft, is that I find I never know if my skin is really clean. To compensate, I double my rinsing process until there is no question in my mind that all of the soap and toner I've used are gone.

Because summer is the time of holidays, of hours spent in the swimming pool or lying in the sun, hair can also be a problem. It might be the time to think about buying a great wig to make the transition from sun-filled days to romantic nights under the stars. Remember, though, that even a lightweight wig will make your scalp perspire. Take your wig off after a few hours, and let your hair and scalp breathe.

Speaking of those hours in the sun, don't forget that protection is paramount. Use a good moisturizing sun block to protect your skin. Don't forget the backs of your hands when you're applying it. This will prevent freckles—all too soon they turn into age spots. From eleven in the morning until two in the afternoon, the rays of the sun are harsh and damaging. Plan to spend these hours sitting under an umbrella by the side of the pool playing gin rummy or catching up with a light novel. And don't forget to wear a hat or visor at all times when you're in the sun to protect the sensitive skin of your face.

Fall

After Labor Day, although the weather is still lovely, I always find myself putting away the toys of summer. Onto the shelf go the beach towels, the backgammon set, the slightly grimy playing cards. And, the next week, after the children are off to school, no matter how busy I seem to be, there is always the sense of more than enough time, of a pause between play and work.

Fall can be a time of setting up a new house in a new location because of a change of job. It can be the time for new projects to stretch and expand yourself. It is always for me a time to take a good, hard look at what the ravages of summer have done. What about my hair? Is it a bit brittle at the ends from the sun? And my skin? As careful as I am, I often find fall to be the time to redouble my efforts, to use a sluffing mask to be sure to remove all those dead cells, as well as my usual twice-a-day cleansing, toning, moisturizing program.

I take a long look at my hands and feet. How have they fared the days of sand and sea water? It's usually the time to give myself a leisurely manicure and pedicure.

When I get up the courage, I look in a full-length mirror to see the effect of hot dogs at the baseball game with the kids, pizzas on the run when I pick them up after a soccer game, the McDonald's stop on the way to an early movie. Now that they are in school and not quite so omnipresent, I'll make myself a big salad for lunch, plan an early evening with nothing for dinner, and fast until noon the next day when I can start to eat sensibly again. Thanksgiving and the hectic Christmas holidays are not far away. The early days of fall are a time when I am able to follow the programs of nutrition, exercise and easy health care that mean I will be the very best I can be.

YOUR SKIN AFTER FORTY

The most arbitrary designation is at what point a person becomes middle-aged. At the turn of the century, the average life span in this country was forty. Now, for women, it's eighty. What made the difference? Certainly modern medical researchers have performed miracles in prolonging life, but, in fact, this century has seen a change in attitude toward two simple things: cleanliness and nutrition. And cleanliness has been the biggest factor by far. Once it occurred to doctors that it would be nice to wash their hands before delivering a child, the life span made a quantum jump.

Even in their thirties, though, women in times gone by seemed to feel that there wasn't something quite respectable about looking young, looking good. Selflessness was in, and the goal seemed to be to look as matronly, motherly and unattractive as soon as possible, to fade into the wallpaper unless called upon to make an apple pie or stuff a Thanksgiving turkey.

Think about the age of forty, or more, today. Do you picture a comfortable old party wearing a flowered print dress and sensible shoes knitting in a rocking chair? Do you think of a platinum blonde with too much makeup at Miami Beach, desperately trying to look the way women did when she was young?

I don't—and I doubt if you do either. When I think about being forty, I think of Jane Fonda, Ali McGraw and Glenda Jackson. I think of Sophia Loren, Jackie Onassis and Mary Tyler Moore. Somebody once wrote that at forty you have the face you deserve, and I agree. At forty you have the character in your face that comes with experience. At forty you are well along the way in your own development. At forty you are that much more of who you are than you were at twenty, or at thirty. At forty you are coming into your own. Is there anybody left who really considers chronological age?

I don't. I think only about physical age, about doing the very best with what you have.

This is not to say that changes haven't been taking place. As we grow older, our metabolic rate slows down. Because the turnover of our cells takes longer, it takes the underlayers of the skin longer to get to the surface. The dermis thins and there is a reduction of the blood supply. The elastin and collagen, the connective tissues, are not what they were. The distribution of the pigment cells isn't what it was; this redistribution forms age spots.

The aging process is a fact of life. We all get older, but with proper nutrition, cleanliness and adequate exercise to keep our energy and endurance at the highest possible level, we can look and feel as good as we can. One of the ways to do this is to rethink the way we take care of our skin and what makeup we use and don't use.

Your Cleanser

As the skin begins to show the first signs of aging, such as lines, age spots, etc., the impulse is to double and redouble the effort with more cleaning, more toning, more moisturizing. Instead, experts recommend that cleansing with soap and water be done gently only in the evening to remove makeup and pollutants. Then tone and moisturize. Don't use soap and water in the morning, just rinse your face well with tepid water, then tone and moisturize.

Your Foundation

During the forties, skin that has always been controllable suddenly becomes oily and dry at the same time. Your foundation now can even the skin tone and texture, giving you a smooth surface to shape and form.

Your Eye Makeup

Because eyelids tend to become a bit crepey, it is wise to use powder shadows which, unlike cream shadows, won't sink into the tiny lines. Darker shades should be used only at the outside corners.

Blusher

Powders are the most natural looking blushers, and the easiest to work with. If you are letting your hair go gray, choose softer tones.

Powder

You may find that your powder begins to collect in the fine lines of your face. If you use a thin layer of moisturizer before you apply your powder, you will find it stays on the surface of your skin. Apply powder very lightly, and then reapply if necessary.

Lipstick

You may find that shiny lipsticks and glosses bleed into the fine lines that have begun to appear around your mouth. This can be avoided by outlining the mouth with a hard wax pencil and filling in your lips with a matte lipstick.

Moisturizer

Because older skin doesn't retain water as well as younger skin, be sure to dampen your face before applying your moisturizer.

YOUR SKIN AFTER FIFTY

Your Cleanser

Cleanse your face with soap and water only in the evening before you tone and moisturize. In the morning, rinse with tepid water, then tone and moisturize. Or, depending on the nature of your skin, you may want to drop soap and water entirely and rely on mild sluffing instead.

Your Moisturizer

Be sure to wet your face before you apply your moisturizer and dry only slightly. There are also moisturizers, available at any major department store, that correct the skin tone. If your skin is too ruddy, you might want to try a green shade. If your complexion is olive and sallow, you might opt for mauve. If you are both pale and sallow, you might look look more lively with a pink-toned moisturizer.

Your Foundation

Use a concealer stick to hide spots, and a creamy foundation to smooth your skin.

Your Eye Makeup

Soft, neutral colors in brown and gray tones give a subtle look. If your eyelashes are sparse, use one coat of mascara.

Blusher

Stick with pale powder blushers, with perhaps a sightly darker shade in the hollow of the cheek.

Powder

If you use a thin layer of moisturizer, powder won't collect in the fine lines on your face.

Lipstick

Outlining your lips with a fairly hard wax pencil and filling them in with a matte lipstick will prevent bleeding into the feathery lines around the mouth.

MY OWN DERMATOLOGIST TALKS ABOUT ADULT ACNE

Menstruation, Menopause and Collagen

I was one of those lucky teen-agers who never had so much as a blemish. You can imagine my surprise and dismay a few months ago when I looked in the mirror and saw what was obviously an acne flare-up. Several experts suggested I see Dr. Peter M. Goldman, a board certified dermatologist and an assistant clinical professor of dermatology at UCLA, who also has a private practice in Los Angeles. Over the course of my treatment with him, I asked Dr. Goldman if he would talk with me about the cause of adult acne and some other matters of concern to me, such as what happens to the skin during menstruation and menopause, and what is known about collagen, the latest solution for depressed lines or acne scars. Here are the questions I put to him, and his answers.

Q: What causes adult acne?
A: We call it "adult onset," and it appears in women between the approximate ages of twenty to thirty-five. One of the main factors is cosmetics, and the other is hormones. If the cause is hormonal, there is an increase of male hormones released by the adrenal glands or the ovaries.
Q: How can it be treated?
A: First of all we do a hormonal workup. If the male hormone is elevated in a patient, I prescribe a medication to neutralize it. If hormone levels are normal, there is a broad spectrum of antibiotics from which to choose. If the adult onset is fairly severe, I would start a patient off with antibiotics in tablet form,

then taper off to a topical antibiotic lotion and other topical products, such as benzoyl peroxide, retinoic acid and Vitamin A acid. I also prescribe the use of a nonmedicated sponge called a Buf Puf, available in pharmacies, to aid in the removal of surface skin cells. At first, this mild cleansing mitt can be used every other day or once a day, and then it can be used up to twice a day.

    If an adult onset is very severe, we can consider using a process called dermabrasion, where high-speed rotating brushes or diamond fraises abrade away the top layer of the skin.

Q: What about a premenstrual flare-up of acne?

A: It is the surge of androgens, particularly progesterone, in the ten days or so before menstruation that aggravates acne. An increased dosage of antibiotics can control it, or an estrogen-dominant birth control pill. An anti-inflammatory medicine can also be injected into the outbreak.

Q: What about menopause?

A: During menopause, the circulating levels of estrogen in the body decrease, and this affects the whole system. The hair gets thinner, the bones more brittle and the skin is drier. In most cases, acne tends to quiet down. The skin's dryness can be controlled by using a heavier type of moisturizer, and a water-base, oil-free makeup. Nearly every major firm makes such a product; and you can find them in any department store or pharmacy.

Q: Is collagen the wonder product the ads claim?

A: The important thing to remember is that nothing rubbed on the skin goes below its surface, although the collagen creams have a very nice texture. Collagen injections are reasonably effective to "plump up" depressed lines in the forehead and cheeks or postacne scars. At the moment, though, we don't know how long collagen lasts.

9

What to Do About Cellulite

Cellulite, the localized fat deposits that affect thighs, hips, abdomen, buttocks and the upper arms, has many causes. The main cause is heredity—if your mother has a tendency toward cellulite, the chances are that you will, too. And, unfortunately, all of the dieting in the world won't make it budge. When I was doing my research on cellulite, I came across an interesting bit of trivia. Doctors who examined large numbers of female concentration camp victims just after the Second World War who were virtually skin and bones still had pockets of cellulite.

Stress, foods rich in refined carbohydrates that the body can't break down, high estrogen levels, insufficient intake of water and lack of exercise all contribute to poor circulation. A poor circulatory system prevents the body from filtering away these fat deposits as it would any other waste. Because the body constantly processes waste in the form of these fat deposits, it is impossible to get rid of cellulite.

The goal is not to get rid of cellulite, but to control it. Increasing daily exercise and avoiding the carbohydrate-rich foods that may contribute to cellulite will lower its production. Then you can turn your attention to dealing with the cellulite already present. There are several methods that experts in the field use to control cellulite:

THE WET WRAP

The oldest, and to me, the least comfortable way to control cellulite, is the wet wrap where warm, presoaked bandages are applied to the problem areas. As the bandages cool, the body temperature drops. Companies marketing this treatment advise you to wear a plastic suit to keep the heat in and jump around for the 60-minute treatment. This burns off calories, and increases the circulation to the problem areas.

THE PLASTIC WRAP

With this technique, a special cream containing "hot oils" is massaged into the skin, then a second application of cream is applied. Plastic wrap (the kind you buy at the supermarket) is then wrapped around the body. The wrap and cream are offered by several companies at department stores and pharmacies for your use at home. It's far from tidy, but, again, it does work. Each treatment takes an hour.

THE DRY WRAP

With this method, a slimming gel is applied to the body at a body contouring salon and massaged into the skin. So-called toning tapes are then wrapped around the body for an hour. The skin is firmed, toned and tightened, which improves its elasticity. Also, the texture of the skin is improved.

BODY CREAMS

When I find a hint of that ugly cottage cheese look on my upper thighs or buttocks, what works for me is one of the body contour creams available in major department stores. Like the wrapping methods (but without the wrapping), these products work on the principle of increasing body heat and blood circulation in the affected areas to break down the waste trapped within the system. As bits of this waste are freed, the body rids itself of it through the normal channels of elimination—the kidneys, liver and intestines. A body cream can be applied as often as every thirty-six hours. I have found that after an application I have lost as much as one-half inch on each upper thigh, and that my buttocks have lost their dimpled effect.

I want to emphasize again, however, that any treatment for cellulite is only temporary. No matter what you do, it won't vanish permanently.

❧ 10 ❧

What Plastic Surgery Is All About

As the years go on, the skin begins to sag and droop. Expression lines turn into deep, permanent grooves that can make a face look hard. The skin can look like a spider web of tiny, unwanted wrinkles that no amount of moisturizing can remove. What the plastic surgeon does is pull the skin up and make it taut again. The skin no longer sags and droops. The deep, permanent grooves are once again merely expression lines and the network of tiny, unwanted wrinkles vanishes.

CHOOSING A PLASTIC SURGEON

If picking a hairdresser should be done carefully, no words can describe the care you should take when you choose a plastic surgeon because this is no temporary matter. A mini-facelift, or whatever you have in mind, won't last forever (five to ten years seems to be the prediction), but it is worth the most diligent and careful research.

If women, or men, in your social group have had plastic surgery that has left them looking fresher, better and, most of all, natural, they are the ones to ask for a recommendation. If not, I would suggest you ask either your own doctor, or contact the local chapter of the American Medical Association. If you live in a city with a

169

medical school attached to a teaching hospital, you might check there.

When plastic surgery was far less sophisticated than it is now, any girl who was not entirely pleased with her nose rushed off to the plastic surgeon. No matter what the size or shape of the face, no matter where the eyes were placed or what the mouth was like, these operations resulted in thousands of girls with the same little retroussé nose they had envied on that blonde cheerleader in high school! The trouble was, of course, that the retroussé nose fit the face of the little blonde cheerleader, but it didn't often fit the faces on which it found itself. Any plastic surgery should look natural. No one should ever ask you who the doctor was!

TYPES OF SURGERY THAT ARE AVAILABLE

Your Nose

Your nose should fit your face. If you're thinking about plastic surgery to change the shape of your nose, it is time to be critical when you look in the mirror, but realistic, too. If you have big features, your nose must be big, too. This is the time for a long, hard conversation with both yourself and your plastic surgeon.

After the operation, a plastic cast is put on the nose. It is uncomfortable, but no worse than a heavy cold. Count on two or three days in the hospital with an hour for the actual surgery. The cast is removed after a week to ten days. Pinkness, swelling and bruising around the eyes will last for a few weeks, but usually, even though all signs of the operation haven't disappeared, you will be able to resume your normal life in two weeks.

Your Ears

Ears can be easily positioned in a three- to four-hour operation on each ear with almost invisible fine-line scarring. A tiny incision is made behind each ear. Excess cartilage is removed and the skin is tightened. The ears are bandaged against the head. Healing takes about two weeks.

Your Eyes

Under-eye bulges or crepey, puffy skin on the upper eyelids can be removed in one of the least expensive operations a plastic surgeon performs, and it will take only an hour and a half. Under-eye bulges, or bags, are pads of fat which escape the control of the muscles surrounding the eye. These fatty pads can also appear above the eye, but they seem to be noticeable at a much later date than those under the eye. Under-eye bulges are often hereditary and may appear when a woman is only in her twenties. Using a local or general anesthetic, the surgeon makes a fine incision just below the lower lash or in the hollow where the eyeball curves inward to meet the arch of the bone. He removes the fat and sews up the skin.

The tissues around the eye heal so well that scars almost never occur. If they do, they are so fine you need a magnifying glass to see them. Stitches can be removed in four or five days, and bruising and discoloration is usually gone within a month. If the eyes swell, they can be helped with ice packs.

A Face Lift

A face lift pulls up sagging skin. It also pulls out the lines concentrated around the eyes, mouth and on the forehead. If necessary, the skin of the throat is smoothed to tighten a double chin.

In this three- to four-hour operation, the surgeon works on the muscular bed underlying the skin, reattaching facial muscles. An incision is usually made in the natural fold in front of the ear, running under the lobe, up behind the ear and diagonally into the scalp. Even in the early stages of healing, the only scar that shows is the one in front of the hair, but it fades within a couple of months. A local anesthetic is usually used.

Stitches are removed after five to seven days. There is usually some swelling, but after a week or two it starts to subside. The degree of puffiness and bruising and how long it lasts depends on your own body chemistry.

A Mini-Lift for Your Face

A mini-lift smooths out the neck and gets rid of a double chin. An incision is made behind each ear, the skin is pulled up and sewn into place. This mini-lift can take up to two hours. Again, the amount of puffiness and bruising you experience depends on your own healing chemistry.

Another operation considered to be a mini-lift takes a tuck by the ear that lifts the upper third of the face. If your brows droop and you have lines on your forehead, they can be lifted and smoothed.

Plastic surgery can do wonders—as long as you understand before the operation exactly what the surgery can and cannot do for you.

·11·

Taking Care of Your Teeth

Everybody would like to have a pretty smile, but taking care of your teeth is about much more than that. Twenty million people in the United States have no teeth at all, reason enough to take care of the teeth you have.

According to the American Dental Association, only two percent of teeth are lost to decay. Periodontal disease of the gums causes the rest. Red, swollen and bleeding gums are signs of periodontal disease. Soft, puffy, ulcerous gums drain infection into the body just as any other wound does. Whether you know it or not, you're walking around with a low-grade fever that is draining your energy.

Healthy gum tissue has tiny salivary glands that flush the tooth surfaces with saliva. If your diet includes fresh, raw vegetables and other roughage, the glands work properly. Sticky food and refined white four and sugar combine with the bacteria in saliva to form a film which dentists call plaque. Minerals in the saliva cause the plaque to harden on the surface of the tooth. Inside this shield of plaque, food particles ferment to dissolve the calcium of the tooth. These waste products irritate the gum tissue. As more plaque forms, the body fights back by sending white cells into the gums to combat the infection. To make room for the white cells, the protective gum tissue recedes further down the root of the tooth. By the time this happens, the tooth is all but lost.

To initiate a program of proper tooth and gum care, I would suggest you schedule a visit to your dentist. After an analysis of your teeth and gums, he or she can advise you how to keep them, and yourself, healthy.

My own tooth and gum care program involves brushing, nightly flossing with unwaxed dental floss, which can remove 75 percent of the plaque, and a rounded toothpick to get at the space between the gum and the tooth. Using a soft toothbrush with rounded nylon bristles and small back-and-forth strokes on the surfaces of the teeth for five minutes dislodges the residue. Then I rinse my mouth out thoroughly. In the morning, I use only my toothbrush. Some dentists feel that with proper methods of plaque removal, toothpaste is unnecessary. To me, toothpaste makes my mouth feel clean and fresh.

12

Your Hands and Feet

CARE OF THE HANDS

I have a friend who couldn't be more lovely. Her face is youthful and glows with good health and proper skin care. Her body is slender and supple from proper nutrition and exercise. Her hair is a thick, marvelous mane with the perfect "wash-and-wear" cut. And yet, if you looked only at her hands, you would expect to see a much older woman. There is always plastic surgery for your face. No such remedy exists for your hands.

Because hands can show age faster than anywhere else on the body, you have to exercise more than the proverbial ounce of prevention. Water, detergents and household cleaning agents are all abrasives and they take their toll. It may seem like a lot of trouble, but you should wear rubber gloves when you work in the kitchen and cotton gloves when you do your housework. When it is raining or snowing outside, wear gloves.

Your hands should always be protected from the cold. Every time you get your hands wet, lather on the hand lotion. Rub any excess lotion into your elbows. An inexpensive hand lotion can be used; the important thing is to use it regularly.

Age spots can be controlled. Just remember to use a sun screen when you're in the sun. Existing age spots can be partially bleached out; there are many good creams on the market that have been developed for just this purpose. Tobacco stains on your fingers can be removed with lemon juice or peroxide.

THE NAILS

Your nails are horny extensions of the skin. They grow at the rate of a quarter of an inch a month. The strength of your nails is partly due to genes, but nutrition is also important. Foods rich in iron, calcium, potassium, Vitamin B and iodine will help to keep your nails healthy and strong. Extreme cold, too much sun, the chlorine in swimming pools and the detergent in cleaning products all make your nails brittle. Too much soap and water makes them soft.

THE MANICURE

An expert manicure is essential to the appearance of your hands. To give yourself such a manicure, you'll need:

> A bowl filled with warm, soapy water
> Emery boards—use the fine side to file your nails
> Orange stick with the tip wrapped in sterile cotton
>   (or cotton-tipped swabs)
> Cotton balls
> Nail buffer
> Polish remover
> Nailbrush
> Hand towel
> Cuticle cream or petroleum jelly
> Nail polish
> Polish sealer
> Clear base coat polish
> Nail menders glue
> Facial tissue

File your nails first, holding the finer side of the emery board at a 45-degree angle to the nail. File toward the center in one direction only. Don't file into the corners or your nails will split and break easily. The object is graceful fingertips, and an oval shape looks best to me.

With a cotton ball soaked in polish remover, remove all of your old polish. Dip your hands in warm, soapy water to be sure all the polish remover is removed. While your fingers are wet, use a soft nailbrush. Rinse in cool water and dry.

Massage the nails with cuticle cream or petroleum jelly. Soak for a few minutes in the warm, soapy water.

With the cotton-wrapped orange stick, gently push back the

cuticles. If you have a torn cuticle, snip off only the loose flap of skin. The proper use of creams rubbed into the cuticle will guarantee you'll never have another torn cuticle.

If you have a minor split or a cracked nail, here's how to repair it: Tear off a tiny shred of facial tissue and saturate it with nail menders glue. Place it on the break and flatten it down over the split. Be sure it is flat against the nail. Wait 5 minutes for it to dry and apply a clear base coat.

Apply a thin coat of color, polishing the backs of the nails as well as the front to protect the tips. Five minutes later, apply another coat of color. Let it dry for 5 minutes.

Apply a top coat of clear sealer. To keep your manicure in perfect shape, apply another coat of color and a coat of sealer every other night. At the end of two weeks, begin again.

THE PEDICURE

To give yourself an expert pedicure, all you need in addition to what you already have for your manicure is a bigger basin in which to soak your feet.

Soak your feet in warm soapy water for 10 minutes, rinse and pat dry.

Rub moisturizer or body lotion into your feet. Rub the heels and sides with pumice stone to remove the dry, dead skin.

File or clip your toenails straight across.

Rub cuticle cream into your toenails. Use a cotton-wrapped orange stick to gently push the cuticle back.

Polish your toenails if you wish.

Slather lots of moisturizer or body lotion on your feet. You might want to wear little socks or slippers for a while to protect your new pedicure.

·❧·13·❧·

Makeup—What It Can and Cannot Do for You

There's no question about it; makeup is a luxury. Foundation, blushers, pencils, mascara and lip gloss are to enhance the clean, blemish-free complexion that proper skin care has given you.

Unlike most luxuries, makeup can be overdone. We've all seen a woman, usually during the day, who is so made up that you might think she was trying out for Ringling Brothers. I doubt that any woman sits down to make herself look like a clown; I can only assume that she has applied her makeup without considering what she wants her makeup to do for her.

CORRECTING COMMON FLAWS

Few women are entirely satisfied with their features, but even the most critical among us will grant that some of our features are better than others. Makeup can emphasize good features and this emphasis will detract from what we don't like about our faces.

The right makeup can do a lot for you. It can be a big help in correcting some very common flaws.

If Your Nose Is Too Big

You may want to consider plastic surgery. Many women, however, minimize a large nose by emphasizing their eyes.

If Your Jaw Recedes

Accentuate your eyes with dramatic makeup and let them be the center of attention.

If Your Eyes Protrude

Avoid light eye shadows. Women with protruding eyes should use colors like plum, brown or gray. Dark color deemphasizes and minimizes; light color will call even more attention to the eyes.

If Your Eyes Are Set Close Together

Try to separate your eyebrows a little. If it looks right, tweeze them. Then use light eye shadow in the inner corner of the eye and darker eye shadow on the outer half of the lid. The colors could go from beige at the inner corner of the eye to brown for the outer half of the lid, or from pale green to darker green. Blend carefully. When you apply your mascara, use a heavy hand on the lashes at the outer corner of the eye, and little, or none, on the inner corner.

If You Wear Glasses

Some women who wear glasses seem to think eye makeup is not for them because it is concealed behind their glasses. With the large glasses in style now, this isn't the case. Instead, these large lenses provide a dramatic frame for proper eye makeup.

APPLYING MAKEUP

Before you apply any makeup give some thought to the lighting in which you'll be seen, as opposed to the light in which you'll put it on.

When I apply my makeup during the day, I do it near a window. If I'm applying makeup in the evening, I think ahead to what the light is going to be.

With all the traveling I've done, there are few places short of riding on the back of a motorcycle where I haven't put on my makeup. When I'm in a hotel, I'll take the shade off a lamp and put on my makeup in that light. Nothing could be more harsh. Special rooms don't have to be dedicated to putting on your makeup. If you just buy a simple makeup mirror with lights around it, it will be all you need . . . and the whole process shouldn't require more than 5 minutes!

THE FIVE-MINUTE "NO MAKEUP" MAKEUP

There isn't anything magic about putting on your makeup so you will look your best. Like anything, it takes a bit of practice, but it can be fast, easy and fun. I think the ideal look—except for special, glamorous occasions—is a "no makeup" look. When you've perfected this look, you'll appear to be wearing a natural glow—and just a hint of lipstick!

When I do my makeup in the daytime, I don't have more than five minutes to spare. Within easy reach, I have the following items:

> Foundation
> Eyelash curler
> Rouge or blusher and blusher brush
> Eyeliner/Smudge pencil
> Mascara
> Lip liner
> Lip gloss
> Sponge

Foundation

Pick a foundation as close to your own skin tone as possible. Because I have a lot of pink in my skin, I use a beige foundation to tone it down. If your skin has a yellowish tone, your foundation should have pink tones.

Apply two dots of foundation, one on either side of your forehead, a dot on the tip of your nose, a dot on each cheekbone, and a dot on your chin. (See illustration p. 182.) I use my middle finger to blend it, using a circular outward and upward motion. If you have an oily complexion, you might want to use a sponge to blend your foundation. The oil from your fingertips may give you more of a shine than you want. Blending is to be done very gently.

Some of the problems you may encounter when you are applying foundation are bags, dark circles, patches of redness, and pimples.

Bags

Unfortunately, these cannot be disguised by makeup. The only way to get rid of bags is to have them surgically removed.

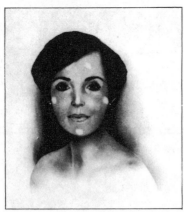

Applying foundation

Dark Circles
If you have dark circles under your eyes, *don't* think that by using a lighter foundation on them they will look better. They won't. A lighter shade of foundation will, in fact, call attention to them and you will look like a raccoon in reverse. If anything, use a darker foundation on dark circles. A good rule to remember when applying any kind of makeup is that light calls attention and dark diminishes.

Red Patches
You might want to use a light concealer stick *under* your foundation to cover occasional patches of redness.

Pimples
Clinique puts out a blemish stick called Touch Stick. It is a tube filled with a very strong astringent liquid with a sponge on one end. Hold the stick to the blemish and apply. It dries out. After you've used this product, you may want to use a dot of light concealer stick under your foundation.

I don't use powder. It tends to get into the creases of my face, causing my makeup to settle into any little expression lines. This does not happen with foundation alone.

Eyelash Curler

I use an eyelash curler to open up my eyes and give them an awake, wide-eyed look.

Rouge or Blusher

Starting on the cheekbone, apply rouge back to the hairline. Use a sponge and blend. A nice rosy cheek really brightens up your face. (See illustration.)

Applying blusher

Eyeliner/Smudge Pencil

You can buy a smudge pencil at any drug or department store. I used to apply it to the area above the eyelashes on my lower lid, but found that it caused irritation. Under my lower lashes, I draw a light line from the outer corner of the eye to the inner corner. (See illustration 1.) Although I use a charcoal smudge pencil, you can also experiment with grays or taupes. The point of a smudge pencil is to make the lashes look thicker, not to make you look as if you're trying out for the road company of *Cleopatra*. Using a smudge pencil also gives the eyes a smoldering look.

If your eyes are small, don't touch the area under your lower eyelashes with a pencil at all. It closes them up.

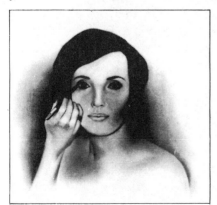

Eyeliner—1

Eyeliner—2

Remember that the farther in you bring the smudge line, the more you close off the eye. If you have medium-sized eyes, just bring the smudge line in to the middle of the lower eyelid. (See illustration 2.)

To make up my top lid, I draw a tiny triangle at the corner of my eye with the same smudge pencil. (See illustration 3.) Then with a fingertip I smudge upward toward my eyebrow, and halfway along the crease in the eyelid. (See illustration 4.)

 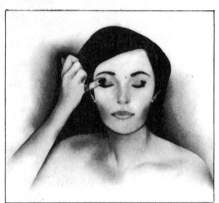

Eyeliner—3   *Eyeliner—4*

Mascara

Some people like a cake mascara and others like a mascara wand. I use a wand because I find it easier to control. It should always be brown/black, no matter what your hair color. Just be sure your eyelashes don't clump together; separate them with a tiny eyelash comb.

Lip Liner and Lip Gloss

To add the final touch to this basic "walk out the front door looking as good as you can" makeup, I use a lip pencil to outline my lips. I start at the outer corner of my mouth and go to the center, following my own lip line. (See illustration.) A lip pencil also prevents lipstick from bleeding. I then fill in my lips with a color halfway between the color of the liner and natural lip gloss.

You'll note that for my daytime look, I don't use eyebrow pencil. You may feel that your brows need a little pencil. If so, choose a color close to the natural shade of your hair.

For a more elegant daytime look, I'll spend an extra minute on my makeup, adding highlighter for my eyes and a different color pencil for my lip lines.

Applying lip liner

Highlighter Cream for Eyes

With my finger, I apply just a little fluorescent highlighter cream on the bone just under the arch of my eyebrow. (See illustration 1.) Then, with a tiny brush, I apply a bit of the fluorescent highlighter cream on my eyelid just above the pupil. (See illustration 2.)

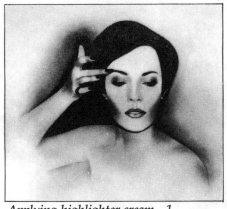

Applying highlighter cream—1

Applying highlighter cream—2

Different Color Pencil for Lip Liner

For an elegant look, I like to have a more emphatic mouth. It depends on what I'm wearing, of course, but I find pink lips to be a nice look.

EVENING LOOKS

If I'm going out in the evening, I add:

> Opaque pressed powder
> A burgundy lip pencil
> Gold creme eyeshadow and a tiny brush

Opaque Pressed Powder

I use opaque pressed powder to take the shine off my nose, cheeks and forehead. I also use the powder over my eye shadow to keep it from creasing. (See illustration.)

Applying opaque pressed powder

Burgundy Lip Pencil

At night, I use a burgundy pencil to line my lips. After outlining them, I fill them in with a lip gloss.

With my burgundy lip pencil (or with blusher), I make three small dots in the hollow of my cheek. (See illustration.) I blend it with a sponge.

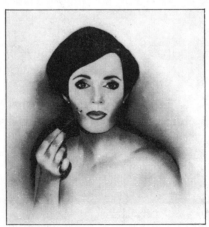

Applying lip liner as blusher

Gold Cream Eyeshadow and a Tiny Brush

A gold cream eyeshadow, which I call my Pot of Gold, can be purchased in drug and department stores. For an elegant daytime look, I use a fluorescent highlighter cream just under the arch of my eyebrow on the bone and on my top eyelid just over the pupil. (See illustration 1.) In the evening, I use my Pot of Gold instead. To complete my thirty-second evening makeup, I draw a bit of gold on my lower lip with a tiny brush. (See illustration 2.)

Applying gold cream—1   *Applying gold cream—2*

Don't blot your lipstick. That's over. Out. Done. So are false eyelashes.

·•14·•

The Questions Women Ask Most Often

As I travel around the country lecturing on health and beauty, I've noticed that no matter where I am, no matter how sophisticated the city, no matter how large or small the group is, there are certain questions that are always asked. At least one of them is undoubtedly something that you've wondered about.

WHAT ARE AGE SPOTS, AND WHAT CAN I DO ABOUT THEM?

Age spots are concentrations of melanin (the substance that gives skin its pigmentation). Eventually, age spots appear on the face and hands. Products have been developed which temporarily lighten age spots, but remember that these products are like moisturizers in that their beneficial effect is temporary. I would use them on my hands only, for it seems to me any bleach is much too harsh for the sensitive skin of the face.

In order to do what you can to protect your hands from age spots, I would recommend that you use a super sunscreen on them not only when you are lying in the sun, but even when you are driving. The sun hits your hands on the steering wheel.

For age spots on the face, apply concealing cream over your foundation, blend it in, and add a dab of powder.

Age spots happen to everybody, sun or no sun. I've got

freckles on my hands and I know that in time they are going to get bigger. I'll use the bleaches, a super sunscreen when I'm outside, and hope for the best.

WHAT CAN I DO TO KEEP THE PLASTIC SURGEON AT BAY?

Look in the mirror and speak naturally. Then see what you do with your face. Maybe you're wrinkling up your forehead, or frowning, without realizing it. If so, make a conscious effort to control these habits without looking like a mannequin.

Always wear sunglasses against the sun to ward off crow's feet.

Remember that moisturizer and foundation not only seal in the natural moisture of the skin, they also protect it from the elements.

If you smoke, you're going to look older. Those fine lines above the lips appear earlier if you smoke.

IS THERE ANY LOGIC TO THE ORDER IN WHICH YOU APPLY MAKEUP?

I think so. When I start to apply my makeup, I approach it as if I'm painting on a canvas. I start out with foundation to prepare the canvas. Then I contour and shade the canvas with blusher. I emphasize and add interest with the eyes. Then I finish it off with my mouth.

The smoother your skin is, the more effective your makeup will be. Once a month, give yourself a sluffing treatment to remove the dead cells from your face. If you prefer to use a commercial product, all of the major cosmetics companies offer sluffing masks, which are available at department stores and pharmacies. If you want to make your own sluff mask, you can do it at home. For oily skin, use a mask made of a cup of oatmeal and enough water to form a paste. Apply, leave it on for ten minutes, and then cleanse, tone and moisturize.

If your skin is dry, liquefy an avocado in a blender. Apply, leave it on for ten minutes, and then cleanse, tone and moisturize.

HOW DO I KEEP MY LIPSTICK FROM BLEEDING?

Bleeding lipstick certainly isn't attractive. Nobody wants to have her mouth running all over her face. If the lipstick you are using starts to run, as many creamy lipsticks do, pick one that is less glossy.

I find that using a lipliner is the best way to keep my lipstick where it belongs, but when I use gloss I find that it will bleed right through the lipliner. And, sometimes, even the lipliners are too creamy, and they, too, will bleed.

One solution is to use a burgundy or brown eyeliner pencil to outline your mouth. They have a harder consistency than lipliners. You can also stop using lip gloss and replace it with a lipstick that is not too creamy.

WHAT CAN I DO ABOUT DARK CIRCLES UNDER MY EYES?

Always use darker foundation under your regular foundation. The rule is that dark minimizes, and light maximizes.

WHAT DO I DO ABOUT A SALLOW COMPLEXION?

Tone it down with beige foundation, and then use rouge or blusher to highlight your face.

WHAT ABOUT A COMPLEXION THAT IS TOO RUDDY?

Again, tone it down with a beige foundation, and then highlight with rouge and blusher.

HOW CAN I PREVENT MY EYESHADOW FROM CREASING?

Use cake or pressed powder, and stay away from cream shadow. Before applying, make sure you don't have any residue of makeup remover on your eyelids. After I apply my eye shadow, I take a tiny bit of pressed powder and put it on over the shadow. That sets it and keeps it from becoming greasy.

WHAT CAN I DO ABOUT LARGE PORES?

It is the overactive oil buildup during adolescence that clogs the pores and causes them to become large. If the cleansing process of the skin doesn't begin at twelve or thirteen, large pores will result, and they're permanent.

The only thing you can do about them is try to minimize them with proper toning. Use a cleanser with an oat protein base to get into those pores. Stay away from hot water. Once your pores are large enough that you start to notice them, whatever you do is only a temporary solution—unless you have a chemical peel or dermabrasion.

While it may be too late for you, you can see to it that your children, if they have a tendency toward oily skin, start on a program of proper skin care when they are prepubescent. When I see that shiny look in the face of one of my children, whether it's one of the girls or one of the boys, it's off to the bathroom for them so that they can wash, tone and moisturize.

WHAT CAN I DO ABOUT JAGGED CUTICLES?

Be careful to cut off only the tiniest bit of cuticle. Basically, the way to avoid jagged cuticles is to moisturize them with petroleum jelly, a good cuticle cream or even a hand cream. Just put cream on them and work them back. You can do it while you're watching TV. This works for the feet, too. I put petroleum jelly, cuticle cream or hand cream on the cuticles around my toenails and work them back.

WHAT CAN I DO WHEN MY HAIR HAS STATIC ELECTRICITY?

The static electricity that renders your hair unmanageable can be caused by heat, cold weather or any lack of moisture in the air. Finishing rinses after your shampoo are the answer. A bit of hair mist on your hairbrush can also keep your hair from flying away.

IS HENNA GOOD FOR MY HAIR?

There are many misconceptions about henna. Most women tend to think you come out a redhead, but there are many different shades, including black, brown and natural, that can give the hair wonderful highlights. Henna has been in use for thousands of years. The Egyptians used it, and so did the Indians. The product we call henna is both a cleanser and a conditioner.

WHAT CAN I DO ABOUT BABY-FINE HAIR?

Have it cut so the ends are blunt. In this way, the ends are as thick as the roots. Condition it frequently. Because color coats the hair shaft, coloring can give fine hair more volume. A permanent can help to make fine hair look fuller. (Be careful, though, about combining coloring and perming. Coloring should be done two weeks *after* you have a perm.)

I don't really think there is anything you can do to make your hair grow in any thicker. Nothing is going to change its texture; all you can do is make it look as if there's more of it.

WHAT ABOUT KINKY HAIR?

The best thing for kinky hair is to find a style that flatters the curls and waves. If you insist, you can have it straightened, but don't try to do it yourself. There is too much risk of breaking the hair. Consult with your hairdresser about relaxers for kinky hair. They are far less drastic than straighteners.

WHAT ABOUT PERMANENT HAIR REMOVAL, ESPECIALLY ON THE FACE?

Never wax on your face, and never tweeze. You have the alternatives of either bleaching unwanted hair so it is less noticeable, or electrolysis. If electrolysis is your choice, remember you must be patient. It may take a period of a few months to achieve the results you want.

WHAT CAN I TAKE INSTEAD OF WATER PILLS TO ELIMINATE TEMPORARY WATER RETENTION

Artichokes, cucumbers, coffee and tea are all natural diuretics.

◆·15·◆

What to Do in a Beauty Emergency

No matter how carefully you plan, no matter how efficiently you organize your life, there will always be those moments when you need a little quick first aid to get yourself through an unexpected situation.

When you've been working like a dog at the office and you're at the point where you're feeling grimy and long to go home, what always happens? An important meeting is called and you have exactly ten minutes to get yourself together so that you'll look relaxed and confident.

If you've spent the day down on your knees scrubbing floors and you have greasy hair, an awful pimple on your face and two broken nails, what always happens? An old beau calls. He's at the airport and will be on your doorstep in twenty minutes.

If you've been up all night with a sick child and you're so exhausted you can barely focus your eyes, what always happens? Your old high school chum calls to say she and her husband will be passing through town and would love to visit you in about an hour.

Under these circumstances nobody is going to be the very best she can be, but there are a few simple things you could do to make yourself feel more relaxed and to look at least a little better. Take advantage of the little bit of time you have and pull yourself together.

195

BEATING THE CLOCK

If You Have Ten Minutes

When you have ten minutes, do a few seconds of deep breathing to bring a flow of new blood to your skin. Do one big stretch, bending over as far as you can as you exhale, inhaling as you stand up.

If your face looks oily, add a bit of powder. Blusher will make you look fresh and rosy even if you feel awful. You'll look more wide awake if you tip the ends of your lashes with mascara. Redefine your lipline. A squirt of breath freshener and a dab of perfume will help you feel a little more confident.

I think it's a good idea to keep a couple of oranges in a desk drawer for emergency situations like this. Eating an orange will increase your blood sugar level and provide the energy you need on a temporary basis.

If You Have Twenty Minutes

While twenty minutes is enough time to shower, put on your makeup and dress, it isn't enough time to wash your hair. What I do in a case like this is brush either baby powder or dry shampoo through my hair to get rid of any excess oil and give my hair some sheen.

Doing a few stretches while you moisturize after your shower will relax you. Do a few seconds of deep breathing while you repair your broken nails. Breath freshener, perfume and eye drops if your eyes are red and tired complete the twenty-minute patchup job.

If You Have an Hour

One hour to get ready is a luxury! In one hour, you can do anything from giving yourself a facial before you shower to taking a half-hour nap with cotton balls soaked in witch hazel on tired eyelids to changing the color of your hair as a morale booster.

Changing the color of your hair doesn't have to be drastic. Use a semipermanent color a shade lighter than your own to give your hair highlights, or wash in the highlights with a henna rinse.

You can give your face a five-minute "steam clean" and revive your spirits by throwing a handful of herbal tea leaves in water that has been brought to a boil; then cover the pot and remove it from the stove. Let the herbs steep for a few minutes; then put a towel over your head and lean over the pot, allowing the herbal steam to cleanse your skin.

With all this time on your hands, the ideal relaxant is a warm bath with either Vitamin E oil or safflower or corn oil.

By the time your guest arrives, you will be as rested as possible, fresh and clean, and perfectly made up.

·►·16·◄·

Turning a Bath into a Beauty Adventure

Fitting a leisurely bath into a busy schedule can take the organizational ability of a four-star general, but the time does come for me when a quick shower just doesn't do it, when I want to pamper myself with fifteen or twenty minutes in the tub.

With the aid of a few ferns, perhaps a little wicker stand with jars of soaps, cotton-tipped swabs and cotton balls, nearly any bathroom can be turned into an idyllic retreat. Add to that a bath tray which fits across the tub to hold the equipment I need to give myself a manicure, a magazine or a book, or even a single rose in a bud vase, and even before I step into the tub, I begin to feel rejuvenated.

Because very hot water opens the pores and lets the natural moisture escape from the skin, my bathtub is filled with warm water. I use a few drops of Vitamin E oil from the health food store, or a few tablespoons of safflower oil. If I want a bubble bath, I use a gel bubble bath. I use a super-fatted soap because my skin tends to be dry. If your skin is oily, a glycerin soap will soften and smooth, but it isn't fatty. A medicated soap will help skin aggravated by blemishes.

(continued on following page)

The time I spend in the tub is practical as well as luxurious. It is the time to treat my face to a beauty mask while I soak. I use my Loofah in slow, circular motions to bring the blood to the surface of my skin. And time in the tub can be used to do my stretches. I alternately extend each leg, flexing thigh, calf and ankle. I stretch my arms, rotating my wrists.

After I have gently dried my body with the bath sheet I have been warming on the electric towel rack, it's on with my body moisturizer while I do a few more stretches. Then I rinse off my facial mask and cleanse, tone and moisturize my face. In only fifteen or twenty minutes in the bathtub, I always feel as if I've been away for a weekend in the country.

17

Beauty in Transit—Advice to the Weary Traveler

There was a time when getting from one place to another had all the elements of a romantic adventure. Travel meant trains, bedrooms where an affable porter did everything but tuck you in, a dining car where fresh roses in heavy silver vases adorned scrupulously white linen tablecloths and the fare, if one were crossing the country, might well be fresh trout taken on at the last stop. In those days, a woman who traveled probably prepared for her journey as if she were sailing first-class on a great ocean liner, with painstaking care to what she would wear, her hair and makeup, the state of her hands and feet, the expression on her face as she tentatively entered the club car for a drink before dinner.

No more. The woman who travels now is faced with dirty, crowded airports, endless waits to get on a plane and for her luggage at the other end. If something can go wrong, more often than not, it will. If I am going to, say, New York, I am not exactly amazed to learn that my luggage has gone to Seattle. If I am due in Denver to give a lecture, it is no surprise when the plane is so late in arriving that I barely have time to grab my luggage and do what I can to relax in the cab. And, let's face it, flying so high in the sky is not exactly a natural situation. A glowing, clear complexion at LAX can develop an eruption on the way to JFK. The pressurized cabins on planes suck the moisture out of the air and out of the skin. Sometimes, the hormonal system is thrown into imbalance and a menstrual period not due for days makes a surprise appearance. I have traveled so much that I now prepare for a journey with a strategy just this side of what Montgomery must have done at El Alamein.

Indispensable on any trip is a tote bag into which I put all the makeup I am going to need when I arrive. This will include foundation, blusher, mascara, lipstick, shadow, and lip liner as well as a comb, brush and mirror.

If I am not going directly from the airport to a meeting, I wear no makeup on a flight. Into my tote bag, I put a bottle of Evian water so that I can spray my face and restore some of the moisture it is losing in flight. I always carry moisturizer to apply to my face, neck and the backs of my hands. I also carry Clinique's Touch Stick so that I can conceal any eruption that might result from the flight. I throw a couple of lemons into my tote bag, too. Hot water and lemon juice will reduce the bloating that so often accompanies a plane trip.

Cotton-tipped swabs, a small bottle of witch hazel, cotton balls to apply it to my eyelids, lip gloss to keep my lips moist and perfume complete my inventory.

By wearing pants on the flight, I can put my feet up on the back of the seat in front of me, which aids the circulation in my legs and feet. And I always request an aisle seat so that I can get up and walk around—another aid to circulation.

I don't drink when I'm flying, but if you do, remember that one drink in the air has double the effect it does on the ground. Cigarette smoke while flying has twice the drying effect it has on the ground.

The nice, relaxing book I take along has two purposes. Not only can I bury my nose in it and use flight time to compose my thoughts rather than talking to the person next to me, but it gives me something to entertain myself with in case the wait for my luggage grows maddeningly long. Not for me, incidentally, are the twenty-six pieces of luggage ascribed to various screen sirens. I carry as little luggage as possible of the lightest weight in these days when porters are seldom in evidence, especially in smaller airports. Twenty minutes before the plane is to land, I wash my face and apply my makeup so that it will be fresh when I arrive. As everybody else scurries to collect their luggage, I head for the rest room, where I take a moment to do some deep breathing to get the blood flowing to the skin. I also do at least one stretch, bending as far as I can toward the floor to get the blood rushing to my head.

Traveling certainly isn't the joyous adventure that it used to be; however, its trials and tribulations can be minimized with a little preparation.

•18•

Beverly Sassoon of Beverly Hills— Part II

When I got back to Los Angeles, I found that the corporation had a new job for me. I was offered a contract as the spokesperson for a new skin care line. Along with the other top corporate executives, I would need to know about these new products from the way they were developed, to the packaging, to a knowledge of the cosmetics industry in general, and our own products specifically.

I had wanted to get involved in the cosmetics industry, but the timing had never been right. On the positive side, the offer would give me a chance learn all about skin care; on the negative side, I would have to give up school. And I had to hope they wanted me for me, and that the job offer wasn't just a way to keep me involved.

I was assured that my traveling schedule would be worked out so that I wouldn't be away from the children for too many days at a time. I was to assemble a team of people with whom I could work.

It wasn't going to be easy. The company was going to launch a whole new line that would include shampoo, a finishing rinse, protein hair packs, soaps for dry and oily skins, a cleansing emulsion, three different toners, two types of moisturizers and, ultimately, specialty hair products.

We started to organize our traveling schedule and I began to do my research on skin and its care. I began to see the importance of skin both in a physical and psychological context. Next to the brain, the skin is the body's most important organ system. It is the earliest organ to develop in the human embryo. The skin of the embryo is already highly developed when it still lacks eyes and ears. The skin is also the largest organ system of the body. It constitutes between 16 and 18 percent of the body weight. In terms of care, nothing is more important than the skin.

Just before our first tour was to start, I went to The Golden Door in Escondido to get ready. Being at The Golden Door has marvelous restorative powers. Everything you should do for yourself is compressed into one week. The food is fabulous, though you get only 500 calories a day. (See the Virtue-Making Diet, p. 114.) When I left, I felt I could conquer the world.

Our little team did its first tryout at Bullock's in the San Fernando Valley. There were really people out there in that audience. I was scared to death and could hear my heart going thumpachunkathumpa. "Oh, God," I thought, "will it always be like this?"

We were a little traveling circus act. It's a strange feeling to be standing in an aisle in a department store in Pittsburgh with a microphone. We created a fire hazard in an aisle at Bloomingdale's. The Fire Marshal came and made us stop until the crowds dispersed.

Somehow we muddled through. The stylist did technical things about hair. I gave my lecture and made the Vitality Drink (p. 15). The audience seemed to like us, and we kept telling each other that the first time is always the hardest. I was on my way.

At least professionally, I was on my way. As far as our marriage went, I felt I was treading water. There were many things that were keeping us together; one of them was David. He was going to a psychologist three times a week trying to work out the problems he had developed. Vidal and I were beginning to wonder if we had made his situation worse rather than better. When David came to us, he would test us as much as he possibly could. He was a great success at testing. I thought I would explode.

The novelty of a new family member wore off and we were all getting down to the basics of living. It was not going well. David and Elan were fighting all the time, and Vidal was going crazy because he had to deal with it. David had gotten thrown out of public school. The teachers just couldn't deal with his behavior. He was transferred to another public school, but by that time I was thinking that to be consistent with his therapy, the right private school was going to have to be found for him. And I couldn't help asking myself how I could justify putting David and all his problems on our own children. It was becoming apparent that the house which had seemed so spacious when we first moved to California was just too small. We found another, larger house, but it was going to take a great deal of time before it could be remodeled to fit our needs.

By the time we started our tour, my knee injury from the Australian trip was acting up. As we flew from city to city, doing our appearances and interviews, I was in constant pain and anxiety. At one appearance I saw a huge mob in one of the auditoriums and I said to the public relations man, "I wonder who that's for." He said, "It's for you." My heart went to my throat, but the audience liked what I did. Everything worked.

Everything worked, that is, except my knee. I finally took a break from my constant cross-country touring and went into the hospital for knee surgery.

I was released from the hospital with a cast from my hip to my ankle. I went to stay at the shell of the new house to oversee all the activity. While the demolition team moved closer and closer to the master bedroom where I was staying, I answered the 7,000 letters I had received as a result of one appearance on *The Phil Donahue Show.* When I could find somebody with a car large enough to accommodate me, my cast and my crutches, I would go out to see my family at the beach house rented for the summer. I was still on my crutches at the end of the summer. It was time to go into the office to plan the fall schedule for my tour. I also had to find a house we could rent in Beverly Hills so the kids could go back to their schools.

The kids went back to school and I went back on the road. Before too many weeks had passed, I was exhausted again, and I was beginning to feel like a prisoner. Our last stop was Hawaii, and I was looking forward to a few days of rest. They had the worst rain in ten years. It was so bad they officially cancelled Halloween!

To make the kids a part of our business lives, we were starting to take them along when we traveled. I took Eden along when I went to Pittsburgh. Not only was it fun for her to see what I was doing, but it was fun for me to have her there, especially since I was celebrating a birthday. We went on to New York where Vidal and Elan were waiting for us.

Vidal was in New York to host *AM New York* for a week while I rushed around, working the aisles at Macy's and shopping for Christmas at Bloomingdale's and F.A.O. Schwarz. Then Vidal went back to Los Angeles and I took over *AM New York* for a week, with Bucky Dent, the baseball player, as co-host.

The main topic in the news was the massacre at Jonestown. When Vidal was the host on *AM New York*, he interviewed members of various cults. He lost his objectivity when the discussion turned to the murdered children. When Bucky and I were co-hosts, one of our guests was the Chief of Psychiatry from a hospital in New Jersey who had just returned from Guyana where he had gone to counsel survivors. During a commercial break, he leaned over and asked me not to mention an execution squad or a hit list because his life had been threatened.

When I called the corporate offices in California that afternoon, the secretary who answered the phone said, "I suppose you've heard what happened." I hadn't. There had been an explosion at the San Francisco salon. There was the possibility it had been a gas leak, and we all put the incident out of our minds.

A week or two later, Vidal and I were at a meeting in the corporate offices when somebody came in and politely pulled Vidal out of the room. The rest of us went on with the meeting. Then I, too, was asked to step out.

There really is no gentle way to tell somebody his or her life has been threatened. There had been a threat on Vidal's life. The phone message had been, "We got you in San Francisco. We're going to get all the other people." There was the implication that the "other people" were the children and myself. The message ended, "Don't mess around with the People's Temple next time."

When we called the police, they suggested we contact the FBI. When they arrived, their suggestion was that we get ourselves some security. We stayed at the corporate offices until a half dozen security men arrived. It was the strangest sensation to be in a house with all those men with guns.

The calls continued. Whoever it was knew a lot about us and the kids and our schedules. There was a bomb threat about the cars. One caller said, "You can tell all the policemen and all the detectives that we're in no hurry. What we're going to do, we'll do anyway." Our paranoia began to build. I got to the point where I couldn't handle the lack of freedom.

Vidal and I went to London to launch the Grey Line shortly after the first of the year. We were back again a couple of months later on our way to Israel.

Because I had heard so many good things about Israel, going there was like going to see an overrated play or movie. I was prepared to dislike the whole experience. Instead, I fell in love with it. We toured the Old City, the Armenian quarter, the Arab bazaars. The sounds and smells took me on a magical mental experience. I found myself returning over and over to the Arab quarter.

When Vidal was a young man in Palestine, he had had the time to think a lot about what he was going to do with his life. Now that we were in Israel together, he was very generous. He left me very much alone, which gave me the time I needed to think. It seemed to me I had missed so much history. What I gained from being in Israel was a feeling of strength and a gutsy attitude toward the world. The struggle for survival there is on a daily basis, and it is a struggle the people have been going through for thousands of years. It was an inspirational trip and also one that helped me see a lot of issues more clearly.

When I first went on the road, I had a vision of myself as an individual rather than as a woman. I would be sensitive to a chauvinistic remark when I heard it, but I wouldn't be offended. I knew there was a problem with the way women were regarded, but the way I saw it was that there had to be a change in the attitude of men toward women to solve it. Bringing about a change in attitude of men toward women was hindered rather than helped, I felt, by women and their new aggressive attitude toward men. I thought that only made things worse.

I felt it would be easier to get the problem solved by working to support equal rights for women. What I stressed when I was traveling around doing lectures were ways in which women as a group could feel better about themselves, ourselves. The very notion that we do better as a united group gives a feeling of strength. It was up to us to deal with ourselves and after that we could deal with the attitudes of men.

The better you feel about yourself the more clearly it comes across in your attitude. You can demand respect from other people. That's basically what a lot of the women's movement is about. Women were feeling as if they were being stepped on by the system, which was run by men. I don't see why women can't demand respect and still be feminine. It's no contradiction to me to be strong and soft, too.

As the year went on, the corporation was reconsidering its marketing approach to the skin care line. It was becoming apparent that the skin care line should be sold in supermarkets rather than in department stores and specialty shops. With a shift in the marketing of the line, I would be doing less traveling.

* * *

After nearly a year in our rented house, we were all looking forward to moving into the new one. Vidal and I were having our disagreements about what should be done. When I was out of town, Vidal would have the swimming pool moved. Vidal would go out of town and I would say, ''Let's pour the foundation for a gym.'' I would leave again, and when I got back another fireplace would be missing. Psychologists have documented the fact that building a new house creates a great deal of strain in a marriage. Rebuilding our house was proving that we were not exceptions. Perhaps something could have happened that would have given Vidal and me a common goal that would have brought us back together, but that wasn't happening. The gap between us was widening.

The house was far from the masterpiece it would be when we began to move in. Everybody was helping, including the security guards who brought along their pickup trucks. We spent our first night in the new house on Eden's birthday, with a cake to celebrate.

There was so much confusion with the move that the kids were having problems. The house was too big for them. When we first moved in, they doubled up at night. They had their own little country club with a pool and a tennis court, but it scared them. I was scared, too. I could feel big changes coming in my life.

I started back to school at UCLA. I went immediately back to a schedule where I was up at dawn each morning to exercise for an hour. With the mental energy I was developing at school and the physical energy I was developing by exercising, I was feeling fabulous.

Another plus was that David's problems were on the way to being solved. We had decided it might be a good idea for him to have a ''big brother'' who could be a strong role model for him. We found just the person. We also found the right school.

After I started the fall quarter at UCLA, I was approached by the women who had organized the Rape Treatment Center in Santa Monica. They asked me to become a member of their advisory board. They were giving a fund raiser, and I volunteered the use of the house. It was the beginning of my involvement with women's groups and women's causes.

I was the happiest at school. After my classes were over, I would stay at school to study. It seemed as if I was spending more and more of my time there. Applying to law school was very much on my mind. There was the unconscious thought that I was going to need something to fall back on, though I wasn't admitting even to myself that there was anything to fall back from.

A couple of years earlier when I was thinking about a divorce, I went alone to a marriage counselor. As I sat in his office, I burst into tears. "How do we do this?" I asked him. "Do I come back?" He said that I would know: He was right. What I was trying to deal with were my feelings of guilt. I felt guilty about wanting to end my marriage. I felt guilty about accepting a position with the company where I knew I would grow, but which might look as if I were thinking more of myself than the corporation. I felt guilty about David. I felt guilty that the other kids were forced to deal with him. I was appalled to find that I was beginning to feel myself developing a tough exterior. I was so afraid of that. I feel I can hold my own now, but I don't feel I have to be tough to do it.

One day when I walked out of the marriage counselor's office, I decided that it was up to me to get control of my own life. Nobody was going to do it for me. I was going to stop feeling guilty, and that was that. I put my marriage on hold.

After I had been at UCLA for a couple of months, I was admitting to myself that I was thinking again about a divorce. It was starting to show. By the time I was doing the last photo sessions with Vidal, I was really resenting being used as an accessory to his life. Not only was I being stingy with my time, I was feeling stingy. It was my identity. I felt my own identity. It was an explosive feeling.

Thinking about getting a divorce and doing it are two different things. I was thirty-three years old. If I divorced Vidal, I would be a single parent with four children. The time would come when I would have to get back into life, to go out again with men. I didn't know if I was prepared for that. And I hated to be thinking about getting a divorce at all. Vidal is a kind, gentle person. He had put everything he had into his relationship with the children and me. Knowing that made me feel disloyal and ungrateful.

What happened to Vidal and me over the years is a familiar story. We grew apart. You can like a person, you can still respect him enormously, but once that magical element that makes you a couple is gone, everything else becomes mechanical. At that point, you're merely two people sharing the same roof.

I knew I had to ask for a divorce one day when I was walking across the campus at UCLA with an armload of books. I had to go forward with all of the fears and anxieties that such a monumental decision implies. There was nothing left for me to do but take the appropriate steps to untangle what had become so entangled over thirteen years of marriage and four children. I found a phone booth and called Vidal at the office. I told him I had to talk to him that night.

Our conversation that evening as we dressed to go out to dinner was as light as it would have been if it had been any other night. Still, I felt a sense of heightened awareness . . . of the beautiful master suite . . . of the texture of the clothes I was putting on . . . of my every thought. It was as if it were the last time I would ever be in that room.

When we were seated at our favorite restaurant, we started to talk about the little things married couples talk about: the children, our friends, the threads in the fabric of our lives together. I'm not sure what I said, but somehow the words came out. All I knew was that it was unfair to all of us to put off the decision to divorce any longer, no matter what the consequences. The words were finally spoken.

My birthday fell a couple of nights after Vidal and I had decided to get a divorce. The kids were throwing a celebration dinner for me. They had sent out invitations, including one to my parents, requesting that everybody come dressed for dinner. Each child was allowed to order his favorite food. We ate by candlelight in the dining room.

My mother's reaction when I told her Vidal and I were getting a divorce was basic Mother. She said she would stand by me whatever I wanted to do. Both she and my father were uncomfortable at that lovely birthday dinner, and I felt the tears in my eyes as I realized that no birthday celebration of mine would ever be quite like this one again.

The children, of course, were aware that we weren't happy together. They heard the arguments; they saw my impatience. A couple of nights after my birthday dinner, we called Catya and Elan in to break the news to them. Vidal did most of the talking. He told them that the two of us had decided it would be better for all of us if he and I were to live separately. He and I would go our own ways, but the two of us would always be there as a unit for them.

At first, they didn't say anything. Then, like the regular kids they are, they said, "If we have two houses, can we have two bicycles?" We asked them not to tell the little ones for awhile. That was, perhaps, a big burden to put on them, but it was a part of their growing up. They took on that responsibility. Our talk with them didn't take very long. When they got up to leave the room, Elan said, "Thank you."

"What are you thanking us for?" Vidal asked.

"For treating us like adults," he said.

They left the room. What I felt was a mixture of guilt and relief and, ahead somewhere, the fear of what was to happen in the future. Vidal moved into the guest house, and I got my first taste of being alone in the big house with the children.

We had a big tree that Christmas and the usual festivities as the children opened their presents. Vidal and I had both been separately invited to the same Christmas party. Neither of us had a date so we decided we might as well go together.

On New Year's Eve, I went to a party alone. I really thought that if this was any indication of what the rest of the year was going to be like, I wanted no part of it. I was really feeling sorry for myself. There are times when you feel so psychologically down that nothing helps to make you feel better. That was one of them. But I had made my decision and I was going to have to learn to live with it. For better or worse, I had decided to be Beverly.

·19·

The Bottom Line for Beauty

No matter how busy my day or how harried I feel, there are certain essentials that I've come to think of as ''The Bottom Line for Beauty.'' These are the things I feel *must* be done every day. Incorporate them into your daily routine and you'll be sure you're at your best with the least possible effort.

STRETCHING

Nothing is more important to me in my own daily beauty routine than the simple stretching exercises I do, not only to give me the feeling I am firming up, but to increase my confidence. I stretch while I am still in bed, while I take my lukewarm shower, while I moisturize my body, and even as I clean my teeth.

DEEP BREATHING

A minute of deep breathing in the morning is also essential. It increases my circulation and it makes my skin glow. I do another few seconds of deep breathing in the afternoon when fatigue hits. I also do one big stretch, bending over as far as I can.

(continued on following page)

SKIN CARE

The house would have to be burning down before I would pass on cleaning, toning and mositurizing my face, both in the morning and before I go to bed.

POSTURE

As I hurry through the activities of my day, I remember to stand tall, with my shoulders back and my stomach tucked in. I never forget that my carriage says a great deal about the way I feel about myself. And I walk briskly to burn off calories.

NUTRITION

I try very hard to provide my body with proper fuel: I select lean meat, poultry or fish, leafy green vegetables, yellow vegetables, dairy products and a minimum of the starchy foods that translate into pounds. If I do succumb to a piece of chocolate cake, I compensate by being extra careful the next day. And, when afternoon fatigue hits, I'll have an orange rather than a candy bar to restore my blood sugar level and my energy.

MAKEUP

With a clean, glowing face, I feel the only makeup essentials I need are a mascara wand, a taupe or charcoal pencil for eyeshadowing, blusher and lip gloss.

20

Epilogue

We had moved into our beautiful new house in June. By the time of the catastrophic first months of 1980, only six months later, it was on the market and real estate salespeople began to show it to prospective buyers. Months earlier, I had been approached by a speaker's bureau to tour the country lecturing on health and beauty. The corporation hadn't wanted me to do it. Now that I was on my own, I took them up on it.

There was no Vidal Sassoon, Inc., behind me now. There were no products with which I was involved. There was no Vidal and his great charisma, either. It was only me, Beverly, and everything I had learned about health and beauty over the years. Whether I would be accepted just for myself and my own expertise was very much on my mind as I began my first lecture tour. It was reassuring when I found that I was.

Meanwhile, law school was very much on my mind. I had two choices. I could either finish my senior year at UCLA and go into law school then, or I could apply to a law school which would accept students after their third year. I applied to Southwestern University School of Law. Before I could be admitted, I had to take the law school aptitude test, the LSAT. I added classes to my schedule to prepare for it.

Just before midterms, I got a call from our friend, Jack Klugman. Of all things, he wanted me to play the part of a pathologist on his show, *Quincy.* The part was attractive to me because the character was an independent, young doctor. She had a certain

217

amount of hostility, but she was a person of character, a light-year away from the cute, frivolous, young airheads I had played in my early days as an actress. It wasn't going to be easy to do the part since the shooting days fell right in the middle of my midterms. I spoke to my professors and most of them said I could do a paper rather than taking the exams.

I was up at 4:30 in the morning to be at the studio at six. Sometimes I didn't get home until eight that night. It wasn't too difficult for me to get down the character's hostility. I had built it up at home. And, by the time I got home, I didn't have the energy to yell at anybody. I was so exhausted that one day on the set, I broke down in front of everybody and started to cry. Still, I was happy to be playing the role. I wasn't a helpless, little creature: I could go out and earn a living, I could take care of myself.

The LSAT was held in one of the big auditoriums at UCLA. We milled in, 400 of us. I had my usual butterflies, but I wasn't worried. I had studied to prepare for the test as best I could. If I didn't pass, I would take the test again. The effort I had put into preparing for the exam paid off. I passed, and I was accepted as a law student.

Over the months Vidal and I had been separated, our attorneys had been working out the details of our divorce. By the time I went to the Santa Monica court for our divorce hearing, all that was left was the formality. Still, I was intimidated. For the first time in months, I put on a skirt. My attorney, his assistant, my business manager, and Vidal's attorney, all in their three-piece suits, all marched in with me. Vidal wasn't there.

I was trembling as I took my place on the witness stand. Even though thirteen years of my life were involved, I think the cause of my anxiety was that change was taking place. All I felt was that I was going to another level of my life. I didn't know if it was going to be a higher level, but I did know that it was going to be different. I wasn't sure what was going to happen. The responsibility for my life was mine now, and I thought, "Oh, my God. Can I really do it?"

After the brief hearing, I got into my car and drove home. What had happened didn't really hit me. I felt no high, no low, no sense of separation, no sense of relief. I spent the afternoon studying. Coincidentally, that was the evening of a big ERA meeting at my house. I hadn't met most of the women, and as they started to arrive, it made me feel very strange. As I greeted my guests, I found myself wondering if I had become a feminist. That made me even more conscious of change in my life. The next morning, I got up as usual, dealt with the kids, and went off to UCLA.

Friends had told me about all the stages they had gone through following divorce: the denial, the depressions, the doubts about whether they had done the right thing. I'm still waiting. After a few weeks, when I got up in the morning I found I no longer had a tense face and that awful tightness in my stomach. When I looked in the mirror, I could see that my face was relaxed. I began to like what I saw again. People on the campus who had hardly spoken to me would stop me to tell me how well I was looking. My friends would say I was glowing. It was some sort of acceptance that came with the finality of the step I had taken. There was something there that said, ''And now I know I have to get on with things.''

When I realized I was going to have to earn a living, I considered what I had to offer in the job market. I knew I could speak well, and my success as a student indicated I was reasonably intelligent and that I had the ability to study. What I lacked was some specific training. I knew that somewhere along the line a law degree would guarantee me a living. Taking the LSAT, passing it, and being admitted to law school gave me an option I hadn't had before.

Still, the field in which I had spent so many years was health and beauty. I believed in it, and I thought it was important. Because of my age and my recent involvement with the company, I had to do whatever I was going to do right then. My instinct was that the timing for me to focus my energy was right. There was another strange and heady factor in the equation. For the duration of my marriage, ideas about what I was to do had been presented to me by other people, and I had said yes, or I had said no. Now, the ideas about what I was going to do had to come from me. My life was my own responsibility.

I knew I couldn't go to law school and continue in my own field at the same time. We all have to test and extend ourselves, but we have to be realistic, too. If I were to go to law school, it would mean another three years of dropping off the earth socially. I didn't know if I wanted to do that.

I was also beginning to deal with the social life of the single woman. A lot of women who have just gotten a divorce wonder how they are going to meet men, how they are going to get back into all of that. I had made a lot of friends over the years, and I knew I was going to have some sort of social life. I won't walk into a restaurant alone, but I don't mind at all going to a party where I know I will be seeing people I know. But then friends would call to invite me somewhere and say, "Bring somebody along." I was used to having somebody take me places and I didn't have anybody to ask. I would wind up not going.

In time I did meet people I could comfortably ask to escort me to a dinner party, and men started to ask me out, too. Seeing a man for the first time was really tough. You have to talk. There I would be, telling my whole life story all over again. And when I was seen with anybody twice, the papers said that I was getting married.

One of the first times I was about to go out with a man, Eden came into the room. "Are you taking my mom out?" she asked.

He said he was.

"Well, don't you kiss her," Eden said.

I had talked to the children. I had told them I would be going out with people. I didn't have a thought about a long-term relationship, but they were part of a package and I wanted them to be polite and well mannered.

The children would play Vidal and me off against each other. If they asked me for permission to do something and I said no, they would run off to call their daddy to try to get him to override what I had said. If they asked me for money and I said no, they would say that their father was giving me money to look after them and, since it was their money anyway, why wouldn't I give it to them.

And my own attitude was confused. When one of the children was having trouble in school, I knew I had to call Vidal to tell him, but I didn't want to, because I felt it looked as if I were failing. I had to really get up my nerve to make that call. And I never knew when Vidal was going to take the children, or how many he was going to take, or for how long. It wasn't even decided whether he should call or just drop by. Then he would just drop by, and the kids would have made other plans. What was I supposed to do about that? Was it my place to insist that they had to go with their father? There was total confusion. Nothing was defined. We were all learning.

From the beginning, I wanted Vidal and me to be friends. We were all on uncharted ground, and I knew it was going to take some delicate handling. Those early difficulties are settled now. The ground rules are established. If there is a problem with the children, he's always right there. If there is something we should be united about, we are. We sit down and talk now, and not just about the kids. In a way, I still don't feel as if I'm divorced. It seems you can divorce your husband, but you can never divorce the father of your children.

Once I decided to put law school aside and concentrate on my own field, my career began to coalesce. When I first started to lecture to women's groups around the country, I had worried about whether I would be accepted for my own knowledge, all of the expertise I have acquired over the years. I was accepted for what I had to say, and lecturing is an important part of my schedule.

I began to realize that I wanted to have an active social life, to meet a man who would be more than just an escort. It's always hard for a single woman with children and career commitments to find a man who is adaptable enough to fit into a busy life that has its own priorities. In an interview I did for Australian television recently, I was asked if men are threatened by me, by the things I have done, by all my children, by the fact that I work and take responsibility for my own life.

What I tried to explain was that women, the evolving women of the '80's, seem to be more and more capable of dealing with every facet of their lives, with their children, their careers, their husbands or lovers. If a woman is with a domineering man, she has to decide for herself if she is going to listen to him and give up her individuality. I think today's woman has to be a diplomat. She has to show him and show herself that her career is not going to take away from their relationship, that it isn't going to deprive the children of what they need.

I like my independence. I like feeling strong about myself. But I also like the man-woman relationship. I like being dependent on somebody in certain areas. I think I can have it both ways. I think we all can.

Life is process, change and growth. It seems to me that if we test ourselves and try to do the most with what we have, it is going to make us feel better about ourselves as we work toward becoming the very best we can be.

Index

BEVERLY'S BEAUTY BASICS

Makeup should be fast, easy, and fun. You should be able to achieve the best effect in only a few minutes with a few products. My Beauty Basics will give you a natural, no-makeup daytime look that can easily be made more dramatic for evening.

For just $9.95, plus $1.00 for postage and handling, you will receive:

- Clear drawstring cosmetic bag
- Charcoal pencil
- Taupe pencil
- Brown/black mascara
- Rose Brick contouring blush
- Pot of Gold
- Makeup sponge
- Pencil sharpener
- Complete instruction brochure

To obtain your own Beauty Basics, send this coupon to:

BEVERLY'S BEAUTY BASICS, INC., 12750 Ventura Boulevard, Suite 101, Studio City, California 91604

NAME: _____

STREET: _____ APT.:_____

CITY:_____STATE:_____ZIP CODE:_____

Please check form of payment __VISA __MASTERCARD __CHECK OR MONEY ORDER

Credit Card Number _____

Expiration Date _____

Signature _____
(credit card orders only)

Allow 4-6 weeks for delivery.